MARGARET RIZZA

OFFICIUM DIVINUM

A musical journey through the
Morning, Midday, Evening and Night Prayers
from the Daily Office

RSCM

The Royal School of Church Music
19 The Close, Salisbury, Wilts, SP1 2EB
Tel: +44 (0)1722 424848 Fax: +44 (0)1722 424849
E-mail: press@rscm.com Website: www.rscm.com
Registered charity 312828

Distributed exclusively in North America by GIA Publications, Inc.
7404 S. Mason Ave., Chicago, IL 60638
Toll free: 800 442 1358 Website: www.giamusic.com

Margaret Rizza

OFFICIUM DIVINUM

A musical journey through the Morning, Midday, Evening and Night Prayers from the Daily Office

First published 2013

Officium Divinum is dedicated to Tim Ruffer with gratitude for all his help and encouragement as we travelled together on this journey of prayer.

Margaret Rizza

RSCM Catalogue Number: RAB78
Order Number: B0373
ISBN: 978-0-85402-225-0

Cover photograph: Rectorat cathédrale Chartres. Used with permission.
Music setting by Donald Thomson
Printed in Great Britain

CONTENTS

FORWARD

The idea of OFFICIUM DIVINUM was conceived by Tim Ruffer, Head of Publishing at the RSCM. We were chatting about certain projects and he came up with the inspirational idea of writing music for the four periods of daily prayer: Morning, Midday, Evening and Night Prayer, which come from *Common Worship: Daily Prayer.* Being invited to compose music for these prayer times was daunting but at the same time I found it such an exciting and wonderful project to work on.

Being a late-comer to composition, writing music has been a struggle. I have always been hugely attracted to the Chant especially Gregorian and Taizé chants which have influenced me and which have echoes of both in my music. The simplicity of the chant allows the words which begin in the mind to become, with the constant repetition, prayer in the heart.

Some of my music has been used to accompany retreats, healing services, prayer groups, and it is used frequently in hospitals and hospices as an aid to bring comfort and prayer to those people who are undergoing life changing experiences. I have received such moving letters and emails from people who are having to cope with terminal illnesses; people undergoing long periods of depression and even people in prison who heard the music quite by chance. I feel humbled and grateful to be in touch with people in this way.

I have been blessed to have had the opportunity of writing music since 2009 for the RSCM, an organization which I admire so much. They promote and make available not only amazing educational projects and music suited for big Cathedral choirs but also offer simple choral music for parish choirs with limited resources and it is for this type of parish choir that perhaps some of the music that I write is best suited.

The sixteen pieces of OFFICIUM DIVINUM are made up of four choral pieces with organ, two cappella pieces and ten choral pieces with organ and instrumental accompaniment.

Morning Prayer begins with THE NIGHT HAS PASSED. It expresses the dawn before us, awakening a new day inviting us to pray in thanksgiving with one heart and mind. It becomes celebratory as we rejoice in the gift of another new day.

It is followed by an unaccompanied choral piece OPEN THOU MINE EYES. These moving words express the desire that our eyes be opened to see beyond the temporal things of this world, that our hearts be inclined towards the desire for God and that our steps walk in the ways of His commandments.

The third piece for the Morning Prayer is DEDICATION, a simple choral piece with instrumental interludes with words by David Adam. These lovely words invite us to dedicate ourselves each day to the Lord with our minds and our thinking, with the work that we do, with our body and its actions and above all that we give ourselves to each new day with our hearts and our loving.

The last piece for Morning Prayer is THE SONG OF ZECHARIAH (Benedictus) with words taken from Luke1: 69–79 adapted by Anne Harrison. This is a celebratory choral piece with organ and begins with a refrain in Latin, 'Benedictus Dominus Deus Israel' – Blessed be the Lord God of Israel. This is the moment when, after nine months of loosing his power of speech, Zechariah's speech returns and, filled with the Holy Spirit, he proclaims with an outburst of praise and gratitude this revelatory proclamation. The first refrain leads to a traditional song of praise. The second refrain leads to a reflection on God's promise to set his people free. This leads into the third refrain which returns to the opening song of praise with an over arching soprano descant leading to the ending doxology.

Midday Prayer begins with BLESSED BREAD, a Eucharistic choral chant with soprano descant and variations for violin and cello. As with any chant this one can be used in any way to suit the particular time needed for the time of communion. It can be prayed in its entirety or can simply be sung even without using the instruments for the variations. The mystery of the Eucharist is embodied in the words: "Blessed bread, everlasting life. Sacred cup, eternal salvation".

The second piece for Midday Prayer is THE REAL PRESENCE, again with words by David Adam. It is a very simple Eucharistic prayer which could be sung in a unison version with or without the instrumental variations. It opens with words of prayer asking for the Lord Jesus to bless us and be with us in the breaking of the bread and offering of the wine.
The prayer is underpinned by this petition for the Lord's blessing on our lives, in all that we do, and in all that we are.

The third piece for Midday Prayer is THE TWENTY-THIRD PSALM with words by George Herbert. It is an 'a cappella' piece with divisi parts for SATB choir. For me it is an intimate rendition of a text that I have always loved. I find that Herbert leads me into landscapes of serene beauty where he describes with wonderful intimacy and simplicity the love that God lavishes on me. I am loved and fed and nurtured; I am anointed and my cup runs over day and night; fear is taken away from death's shady black abode as I am held so close and guided by a such love, which, as my praise, shall never end.

The last piece for the Midday Prayer is GLORY TO GOD which comes from the Mass of Saint Benedict. This new mass was written in response to the introduction of the new translation of the Roman Missal in 2011.
Saint Benedict and his famous Rule, written fifteen hundred years ago, has been for me a source of inspiration. He writes with tremendous simplicity and an awareness of the 'ordinary'.
In writing this new mass I have been guided therefore by this openness to simplicity and consequently the music is simple and melodic and can easily be sung choirs as well as congregations who can lift up their voices in praise, worship, thanksgiving, reconciliation, joy and love – a community held together by praying through music.
The Gloria is scored for SATB with soprano descant, Organ, Cello and Trumpet. The trumpet part can of course be omitted and taken over by the organ. It is very much a celebratory piece with a more reflective middle section ending with a big climatic finish with the full forces of the choir, soprano and trumpet descants.

Evening Prayer begins with LET MY PRAYER RISE BEFORE YOU. It is scored for SATB with optional soloists, soprano descant, optional cello and organ. It opens with a short introductory passage on the organ which expresses the rising of incense. This is followed by a solo cello and organ which introduces the first refrain as prayer is offered up as an evening sacrifice. Each refrain is followed with recitative-like fragments which are sung by a solo soprano and baritone.

The second Evening Prayer is SWEET DREAMS FORM A SHADE with words by William Blake. It is dedicated to the Tonbridge Grammar School Motet Choir and was first performed at Westminster Cathedral in December 2012 as part of the Barnado's charity concert. It was then performed by the Motet Choir at the Barbican Hall for the Barnardo's School Choir competition in March 2013 where they won first prize for the senior choir category. The music endeavours to follow the moving simplicity of the words as a mother reflects on the beauty of her babe.

SONG OF MARY with words by Mary Holtby is a very simple melodic Magnificat which would be suitable for small parish choirs or even school choirs. It could also easily be adapted for treble voices only.

The last prayer in this Evening Prayer group is KINDLE IN OUR HEARTS. I have set this as a Taizé style chant as I felt it lent itself to a very gradual build up with such vibrant and passionate words. It is scored for SATB choir, semi chorus and instruments including a trumpet which enters triumphantly on the last round. As with all chants it can be reduced in many ways to suit the resources available.

Night Prayer begins with BEFORE THE ENDING OF THE DAY. I have set this as an extremely simply prayer asking God to protect and safeguard us through the night.

The second prayer is KEEP ME AS THE APPLE OF YOUR EYE, HIDE ME UNDER THE SHADOW OF YOUR WINGS. These are two very beautiful fragments which come from Psalm 17. Again I have set this as a chant opening with serene chords which are then taken up by the guitar. The prayer is interspersed with instrumental variations and concludes with a repetition of the opening introduction.

The third prayer is SONG OF SIMEON with words by Mary Holtby adapted from Luke 2: 29–32. Here the words reflect the prayer of Simeon as he takes from Mary the child Jesus in his arms and gives gratitude to God for granting what his heart most desired: to be in the presence of the Savour promised by God. I have treated the opening refrain which is in Latin as a plainchant introduction. This leads into the men singing the first verse which is repeated SATB. As the song unfolds the verses and refrains are developed using different combinations of voices to give the relevant colours and expression to fit the beauty of the words.

The last prayer of this group is NIGHT PRAYERS with words by David Adam. A metallophone is used to depict the ticking away of time. The prayer is very simple indeed with the first verse praying for a safe repose so that refreshed we may give ourselves anew to the Lord. The middle section has words of praise and gratitude realizing the great mystery of which we are all a part and again the prayer that God in our hearts will never depart and that he will keep us enlightened through the dark night. The prayer ends with the repeated words " Christ my eyelids close."

Margaret Rizza
Sevenoaks, Pentecost 2013

Officium Divinum

Morning Prayer

1. The night has passed

From Morning Prayer, Common Worship: Daily Prayer

Margaret Rizza

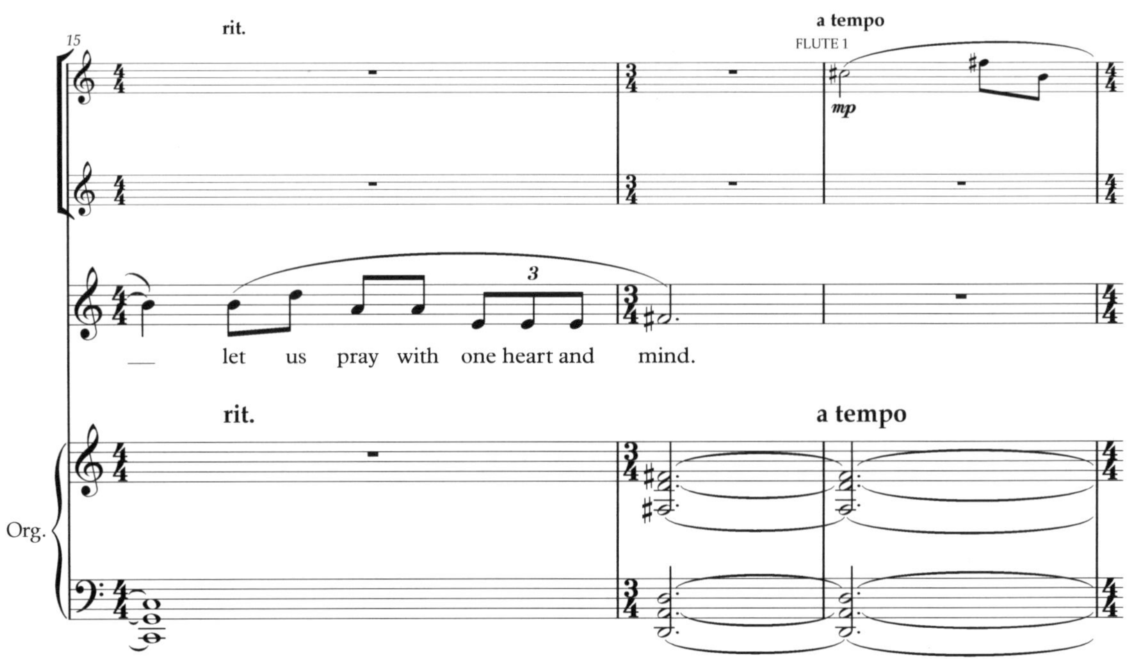
15
rit.
a tempo
FLUTE 1
mp
let us pray with one heart and mind.
rit.
a tempo
Org.

18
cresc. e accel. poco a poco
VIOLIN 1
mf cresc. e accel. poco a poco
Org.
cresc. e accel. poco a poco

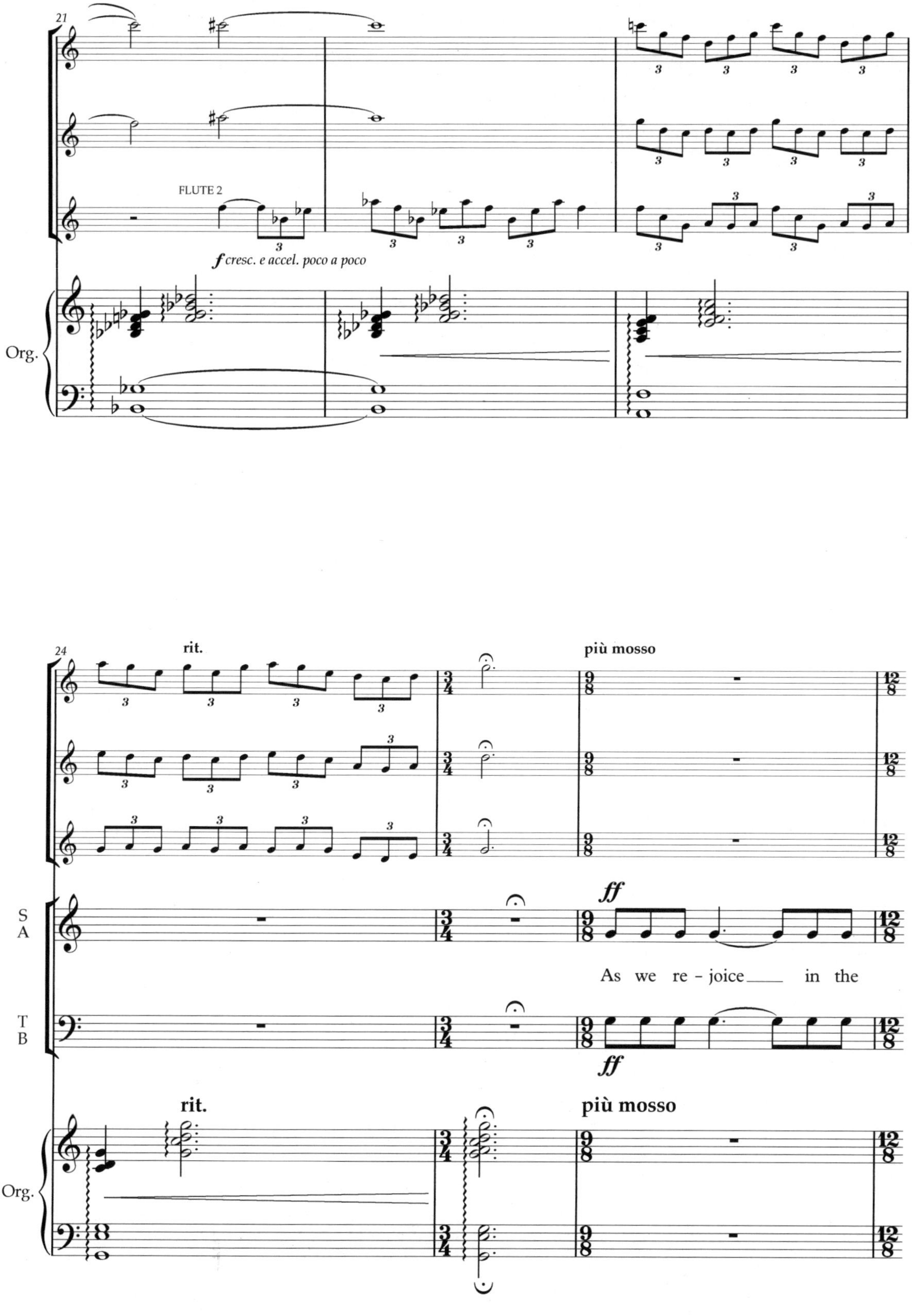

24

rit.

più mosso

S
A

ff

As we re - joice in the

T
B

ff

rit.

più mosso

Org.

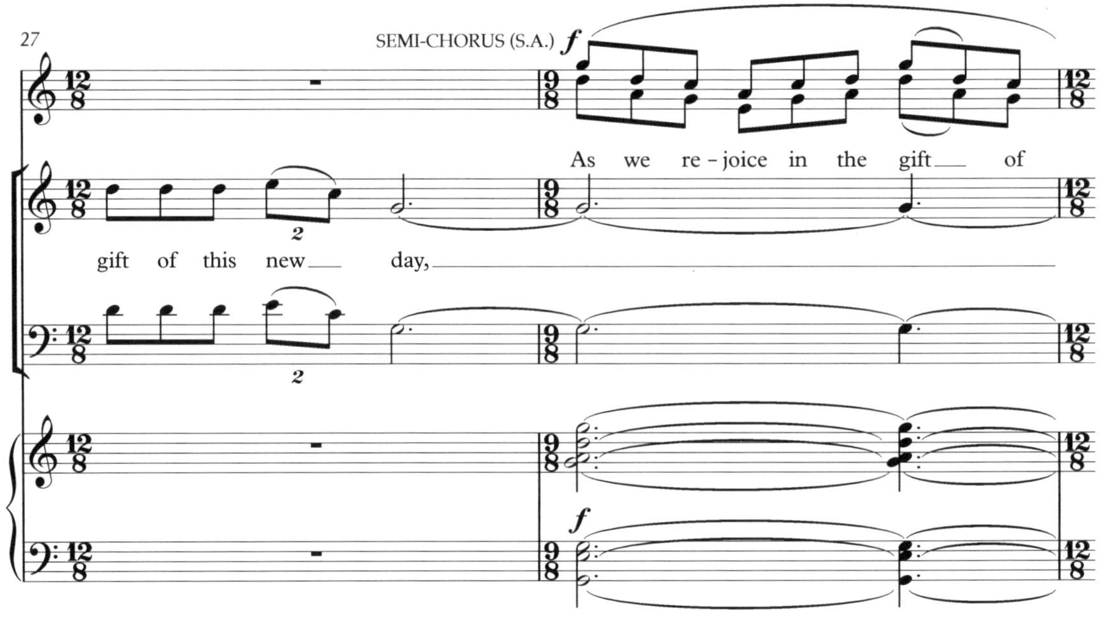
27
SEMI-CHORUS (S.A.) f
As we re-joice in the gift of
gift of this new day,
2
2
f

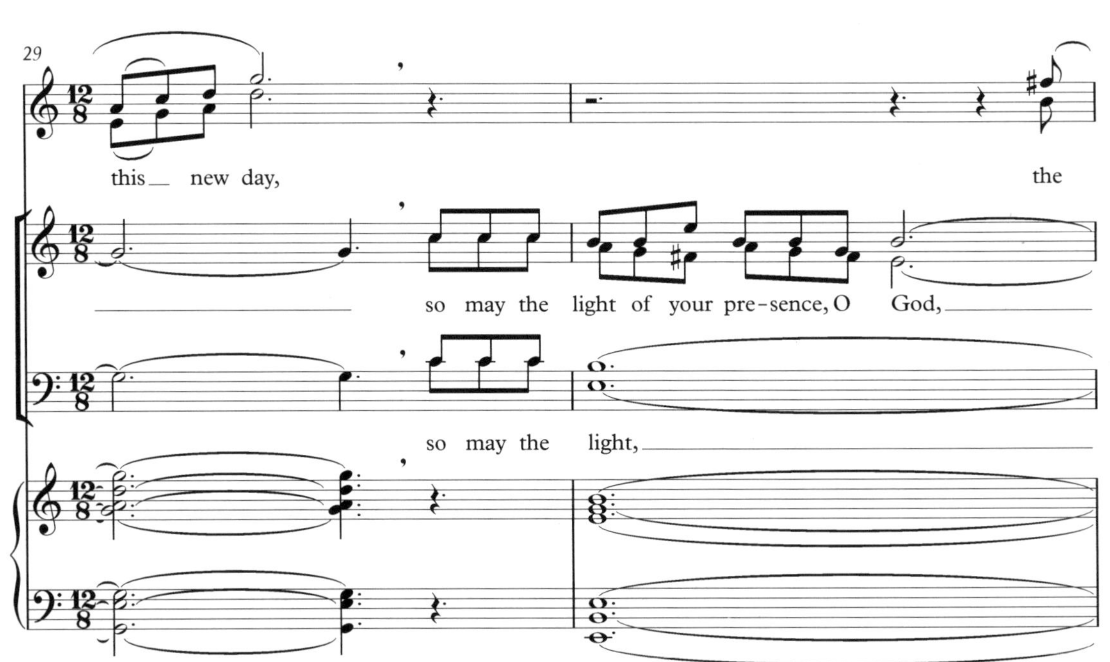
29
this new day,
the
so may the light of your pre-sence, O God,
so may the light,

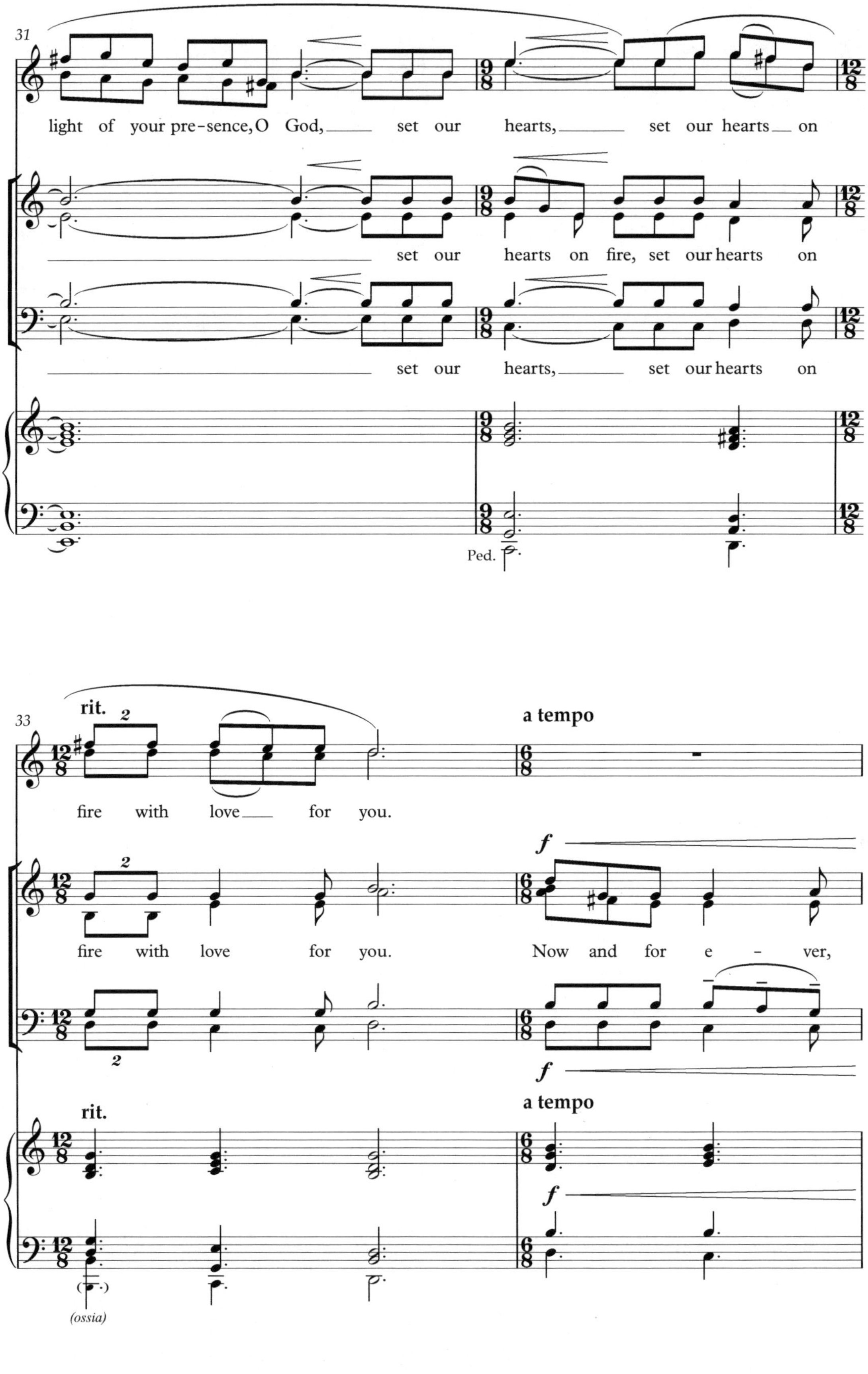

33

rit.

a tempo

fire with love for you.

f

fire with love for you. Now and for e – ver,

f

rit.

a tempo

f

(ossia)

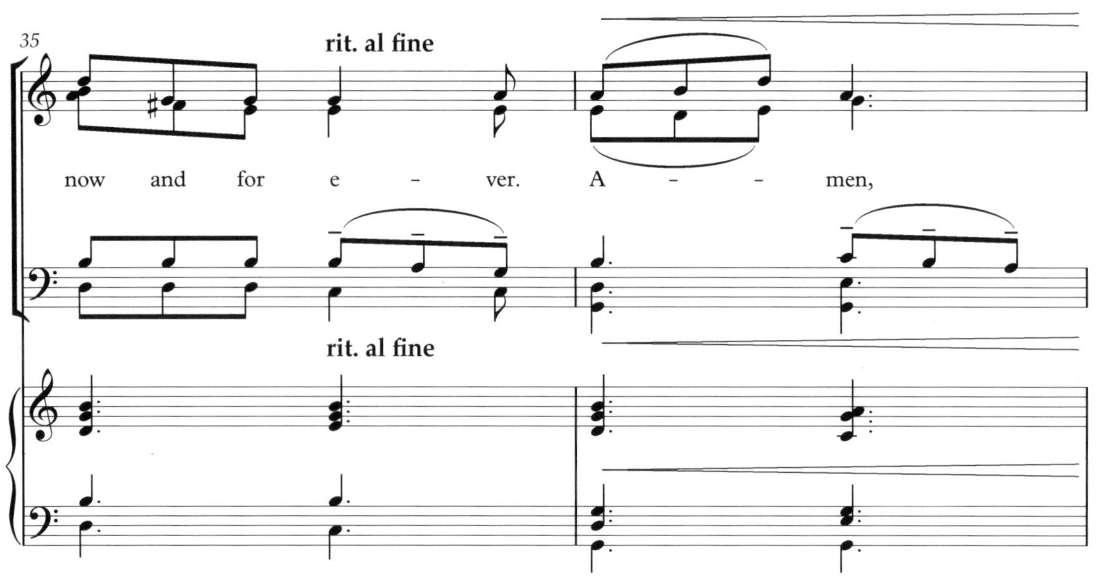
35
rit. al fine
now and for e – ver. A – – men,
rit. al fine

37
ff
a – – men, a – – men.
ff
ff

2. Open Thou mine eyes

Lancelot Andrewes (1555—1626)

Margaret Rizza

Andante e flessibile (♩ = c.84)

SOPRANO SOLO (or Semi-Chorus)

S
mp
O - pen Thou mine eyes and I shall see: in -

S
S
p
Hum.

A
T
p
Hum.

Andante e flessibile (♩ = c.84)

[For rehearsal only]

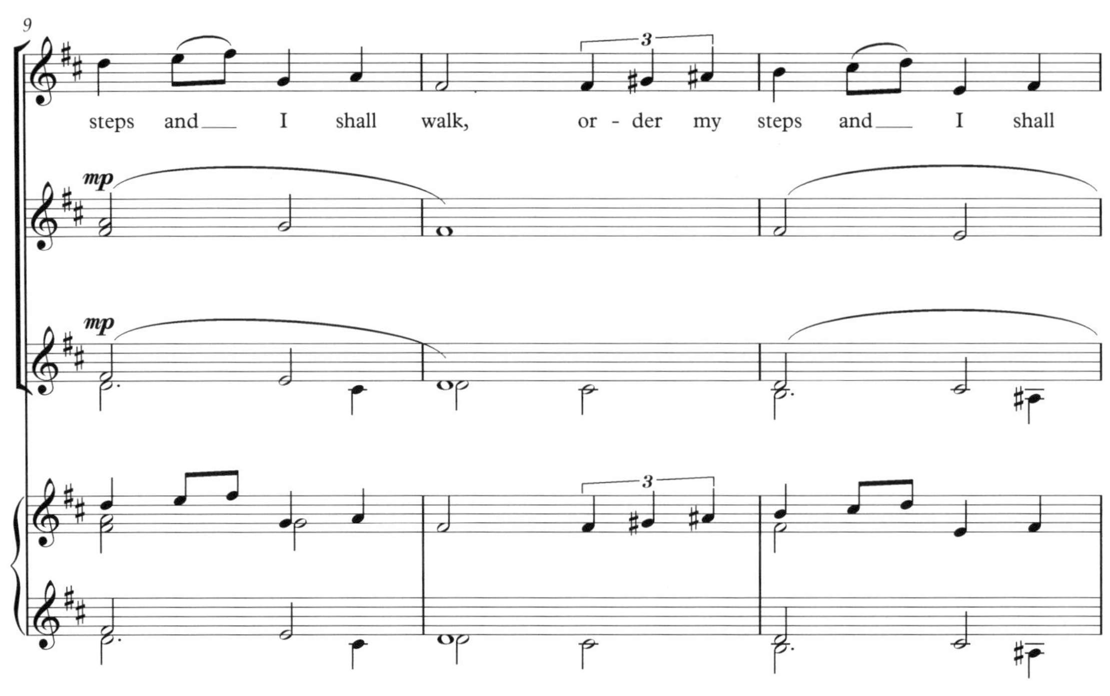
9
mp
mp
3
steps and I shall walk, or - der my steps and I shall

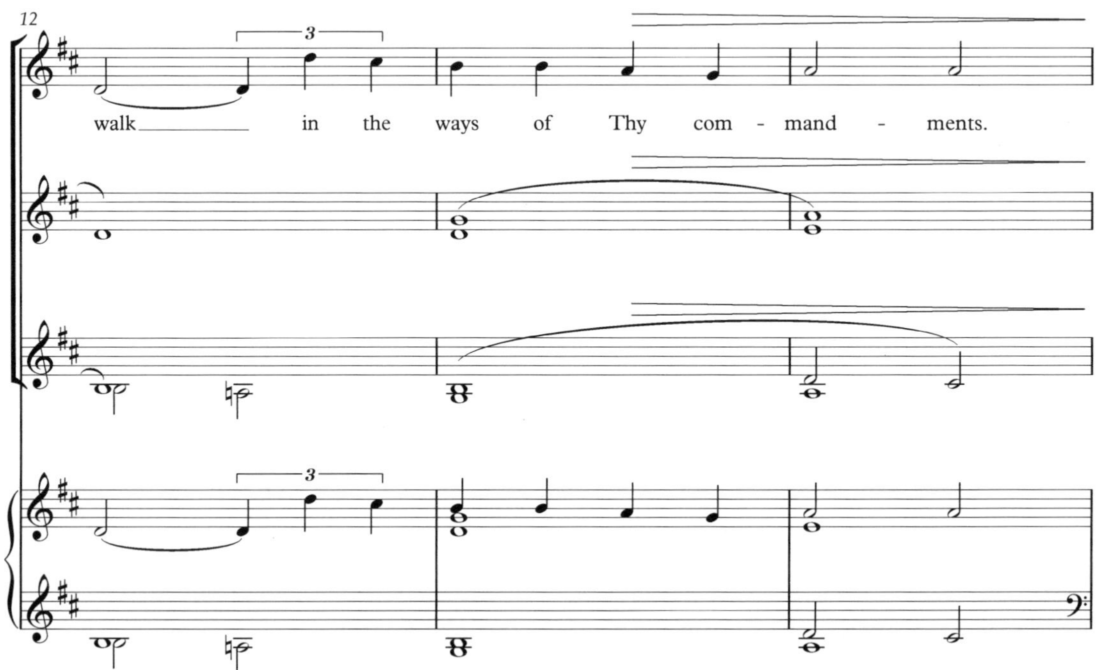
12
3
walk in the ways of Thy com - mand - ments.

15
mp
S
O - pen Thou mine eyes and I shall see; in -
mf
A
O - pen Thou mine eyes and I shall see; in -
mf espress.
T
O - pen Thou mine eyes and I shall see; in -
B
O - pen Thou mine eyes and I shall see; in -
19
cline my heart and I shall de -
cline my heart and I shall de -
cline my heart, my heart and I shall de -
cline my heart and I shall de -

22

mf

sire: or - der my steps and ___ I shall walk, or - der my steps and ___ I shall

mf

sire: ___ or - der my steps, _______________ or - der my steps _______________

mf

sire: or - der my steps, _______________ or - der my steps _______________

mf

sire: or - der my steps, _______________ or - der my steps _______________

26

rall.

, *mf*

walk _______ in the ways of thy com - mand - ments. O ___ Lord God, ___ be Thou to

, *mf*

_______________ in the ways of thy com - mand - ments. O ___ Lord God, ___ be Thou to

, *mf*

_______________ in the ways of thy com - mand - ments. O ___ Lord God, ___ be Thou to

, *mf*

_______________ in the ways of thy com - mand - ments. O ___ Lord God, ___ be Thou to

rall.

30
me a God and be - side Thee let there be none else, no o - ther,
me a God and be - side Thee let there be none else, no o - ther,
me a God and be - side Thee let there be none else, no o - ther,
me a God and be - side Thee let there be none else, no o - ther,
34
rall.
Un poco meno mosso (♩ = c.76)
mp
nought else with Thee. Vouch - - - -
mp
nought else with Thee. Vouch - - - -
mf espress.
nought else with Thee. Vouch - safe to me to
mp
nought else with Thee. Vouch - - - -
rall.
Un poco meno mosso (♩ = c.76)

37
mf
safe, vouch - safe to me to wor - ship Thee and serve Thee ac -
p
safe to wor - ship, ac -
p
wor - ship Thee and serve Thee, to wor - - - ship ac -
p
safe to wor - ship, ac -
40
rall.
a tempo
cord - ing to Thy com - mand - ments in truth of spi - rit, in rev - 'rence, in
3
cord - ing to Thy com - mand - ments in truth of spi - rit, in rev - 'rence, in
cord - ing to Thy com - mand - ments in truth of spi - rit, in rev - 'rence of bo - dy, in
cord - ing to Thy com - mand - ments in truth of spi - rit, in rev - 'rence, in
rall.
a tempo

43

rall.

bless - ing of lips, in pri - vate and in pub - lic.

bless - - ing, in pri - vate and in pub - lic.

bless - - ing, in pri - vate and in pub - lic.

bless - - ing, in pri - vate and in pub - lic.

rall.

Tempo I (♩ = c.84)

SOPRANO SOLO or Semi-Chorus

46 *mp mezzo voce*

O - pen Thou mine eyes and I shall see; in -

DESCANT

S Ah

A O - - - - - pen mine eyes,

T O - - - - - pen mine eyes

B O - - - - - pen mine eyes

Tempo I (♩ = c.84)

50
cline my heart and I shall de -
(ah)
o - - - - pen mine
o - - - - pen mine
o - - - - pen mine
53
mf
sire; or - der my steps and I shall walk,
(ah) or - der my steps and I shall walk, or - der my steps and I shall
eyes, or - der my steps, or - der my steps
eyes, or - der my steps, or - der my steps
eyes, or - der my steps, or - der my steps

57

rall.

walk ___ in the ways of Thy com - mand - ments, the ways of Thy com -

___ in the ways of Thy com - mand - ments, the ways, ___

___ in the ways of Thy com - mand - ments, the ways, ___

___ in the ways of Thy com - mand - ments, the ways, ___

rall.

61

mand - ments, the ways of Thy com - mand - - - - ments.

___ the ways of Thy com - mand - - - - ments.

___ the ways of Thy com - mand - - - - ments.

(ossia)

___ the ways of Thy com - mand - - - - ments.

3. Dedication

David Adam
from 'The Edge of Glory'

Margaret Rizza

SOPRANOS and ALTOS
13
mf
(✓)
I give my-self to you, Lord, with my hands and their work - ing.
mf
17
mf
(✓)
S.
A.
I give my-self to you, Lord, with my mind and_ its_ think-ing.
T.
B.
mf
mf
21
(✓)
I give my-self to you, Lord, with my hands and their work - ing.

25
VIOLIN
mf
mf
29
S: I give my-self to you, Lord, with my eyes and their see - ing.
S.
A.
T.
B.
Hum
Optional
33
Ah
T: I give my-self to you, Lord, with my bo-dy and its act - ions.
Ah

37
VIOLIN
3
mf
3
3
mf
3

SOPRANO DESCANT
41
mf
(✓)
Ah,
f
(✓)
I give my-self to you, Lord, with my heart and its lov-ing.
f
f

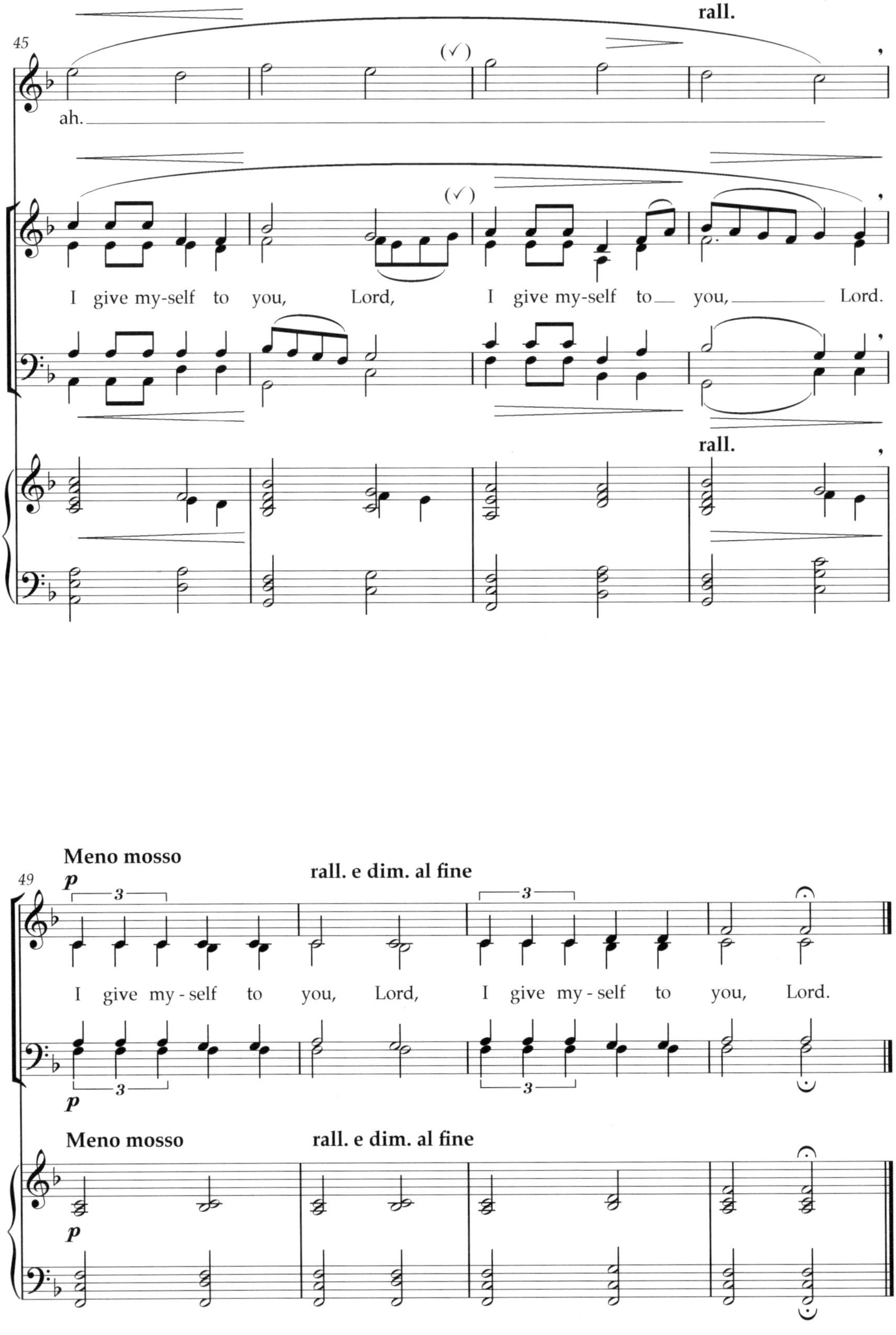

45

rall.

(✓)

ah.

(✓)

I give my-self to you, Lord, I give my-self to you, Lord.

rall.

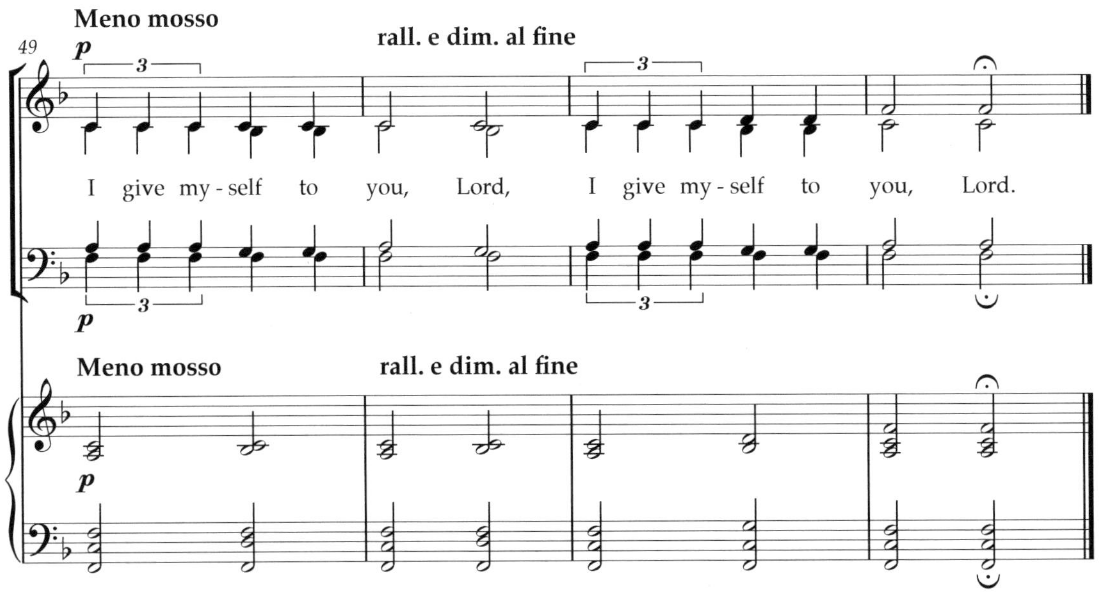

4. The Song of Zechariah (Benedictus)

Taken from Luke 1: 68 — 79
adapted by Anne Harrison

Margaret Rizza

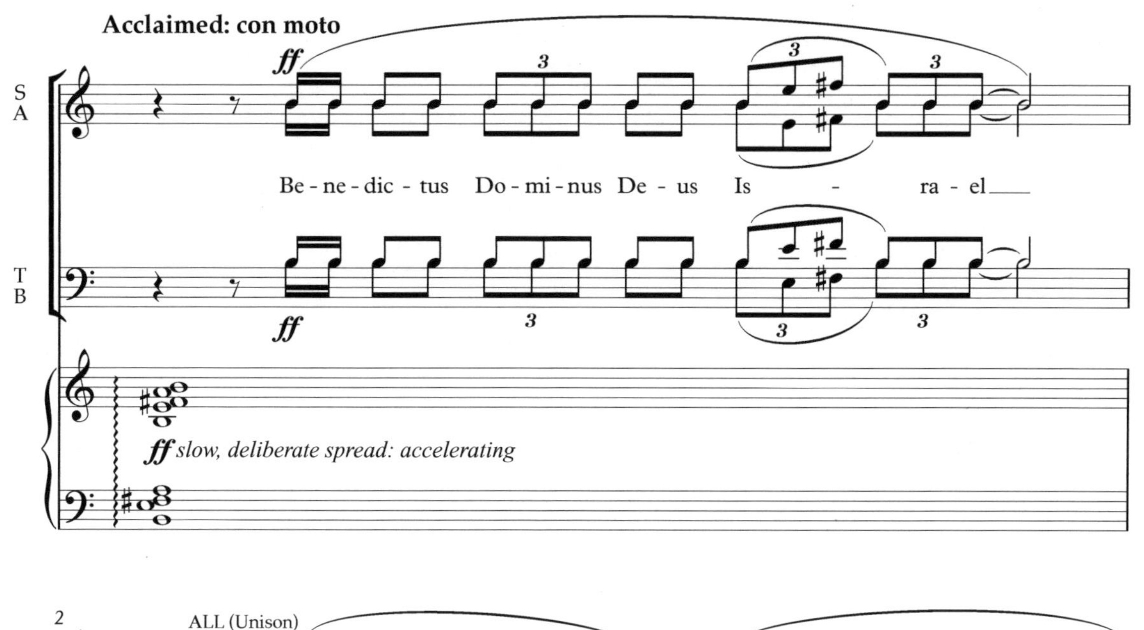

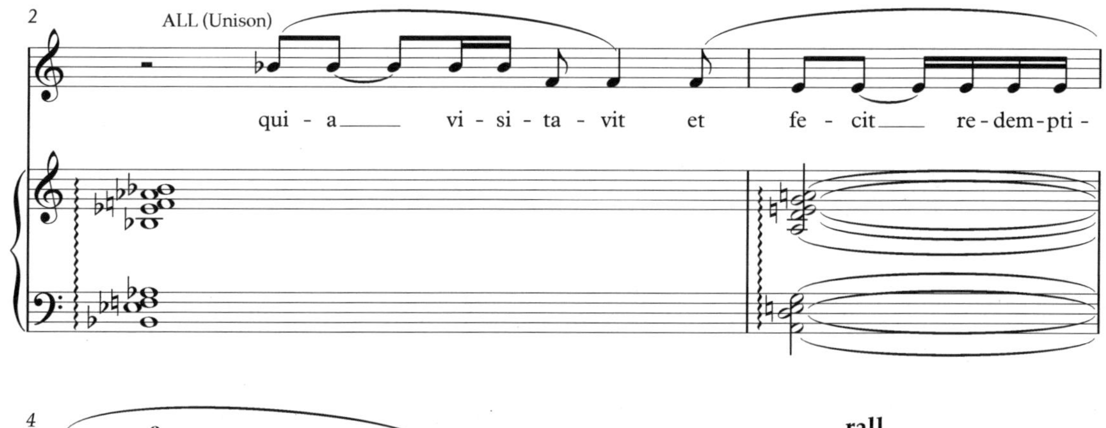

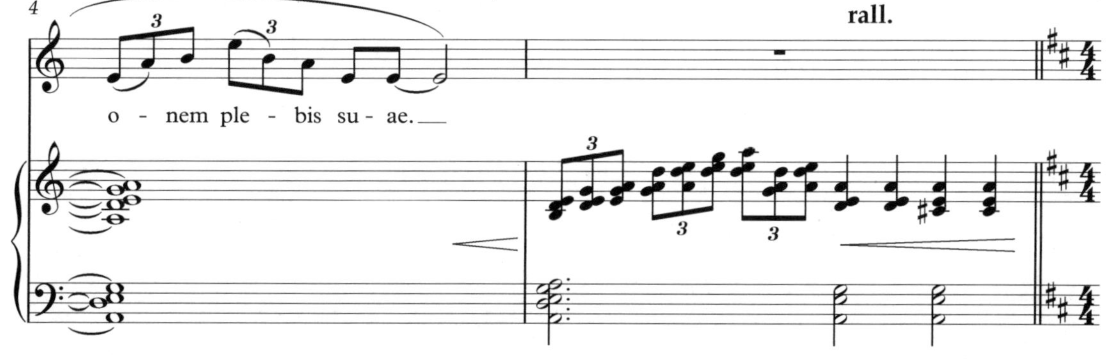

Allegretto con moto (♩ = c.104)
ALL (Unison)
Bless the Lord, the God of Is - ra - el, who has come to set us free.
SOPRANOS and ALTOS
He has raised for us a Sa - viour sprung from roy - al Da - vid's tree.
TENORS and BASSES
Through his pro - phets God has spo - ken of the hope the Christ would bring;
ALL (Unison)
of his faith - ful - ness and mer - cy let each ge - ne - ra - tion sing.

Acclaimed: con moto
S
A
T
B
Be - ne - dic - tus Do - mi - nus De - us Is - ra - el
ALL (Unison)
qui - a vi - si - ta - vit et fe - cit re - dem - pti -
o - nem ple - bis su - ae.
molto rall. e dim.
rit.

Meno mosso (♪ = 108) (♩. = c.44)
28
rit.
a tempo
S
A
mf
Long a - go God made a pro - mise: he would set his peo - ple free, that in
T
B
mf
(Optional accompaniment)
mf
32
all our life and wor - - ship we might know true
35
rit.
mp
a tempo
li - ber - ty, to be ho - ly, to be right - eous in his sight, to be
mp
mp

38
rit.
a tempo
mf
ho - ly and right-eous through - out our days; now this child will
mf
41
rit.
be a her - ald, mak - ing rea - dy all God's ways.
Acclaimed: con moto
44
ff
Be - ne - dic - tus Do - mi - nus De - us Is - ra - el
ff
ff

45
ALL (Unison)
qui-a vi-si-ta-vit et fe-cit re-dem-pti - o - nem ple - bis su-ae.
SOPRANO DESCANT
48
ff
Al - le - lu - ia, al - le -
(or 'Ah')
ALL OTHER VOICES (Unison)
ff
Let all peo - ple know sal - va - tion through for - give - ness
ff
51
lu - ia, al - le - lu - ia,
SOPRANOS and ALTOS (Unison)
of their sin, as our God in his com - pas - sion

54
al - - le - lu - ia. Al - - le -
TENORS and BASSES (Unison)
bids a shin - ing dawn be - gin. So may_ all who dwell in
57
lu - ia, al - le - - lu - ia,
dark - ness see the sha - dows dis - ap - pear
60
(ossia)
al - le - lu - ia, al - le - lu - ia.
ALL (Unison)
while_ he guides our feet in path - ways where_ his peace is_ e - ver_ near.

Meno mosso
64
ALL (Unison) ff
To the Fa - ther be all glo - ry with the Spi - rit and the Son, as it
ff
66
rall.
was, is now and shall be while e - ter - nal a - - ges run.
Larghetto
molto rall. al fine
SOPRANO DESCANT
68
ff
A - men, a - men, a - men.
ALL (Unison)
ff
A - men, a - men, a - men.
Larghetto
molto rall. al fine
ff

Midday Prayer

5. Blessed Bread

Margaret Rizza,
based on the Eucharist

Margaret Rizza

Chant 1

Chant 2

Chant 3

Chant 4

Double Chant 5

37
CELLO (Optional)
arco (or pizz. ad lib.)
mp

41
'Ah' or Hum
mf

45

(ossia)

arco

Chant 6

Un poco meno mosso

CHORALE

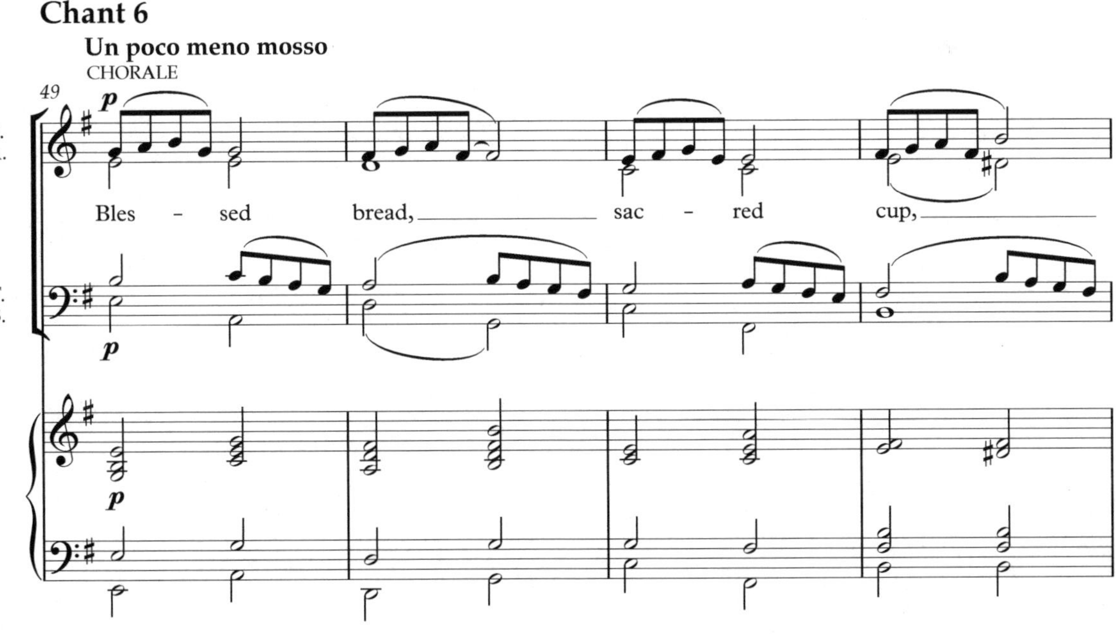

Double Chant 7

61
ah,
bles - sed bread, sac - red cup.

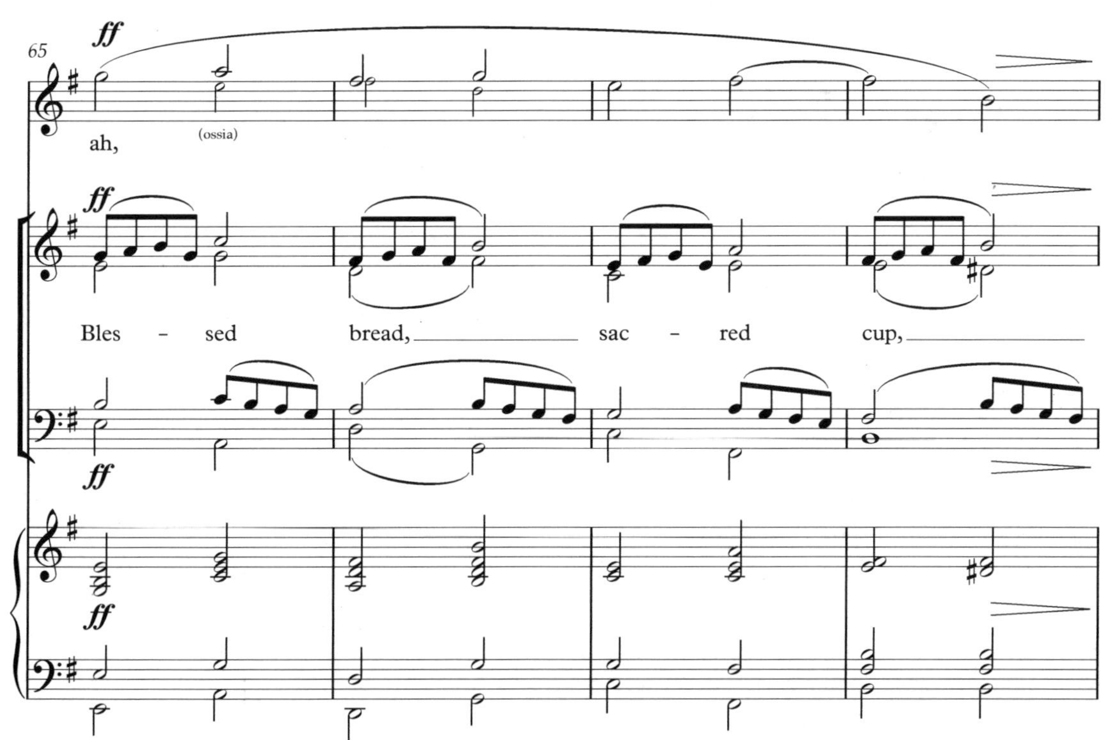
65
ff
ah,
(ossia)
ff
Bles - sed bread, sac - red cup,
ff
ff

69
mp
ah,
mp
bles - sed bread, sac - red cup.
mp
mp
Chant 8
SOPRANOS
73
mp
Bles - sed bread, e - ver - last - ing life; sac - red cup, e - ter - nal sal - va - tion.
mp
77
Bles - sed bread, e - ver - last - ing life; sac - red cup, e - ter - nal sal - va - tion.

Chant 9

81
p
Bles - sed bread, e - ver - last - ing life;
p
p
85
sac - red cup, e - ter - nal sal va - tion, e -
89
rit. al Fine
ter - nal, e - ter - nal sal - va - - tion.
rit. al Fine

6. The Twenty-Third Psalm

George Herbert (1593—1633)

Margaret Rizza

9

mp

God of love my shep - herd is, my shep - - - -

God of love my shep - herd is, my shep - - - -

mf

God of love my shep - herd is; the God of love my 3

God of love my shep - herd is, my shep - - - -

12

mp leggiero

- herd is and he that doth me feed; while he is mine and

mp

- herd is and he that doth me feed; while he is mine and

mp

shep - herd is and he that doth me feed; while he is mine and

mp

- herd is and he that doth me feed; while he is mine and

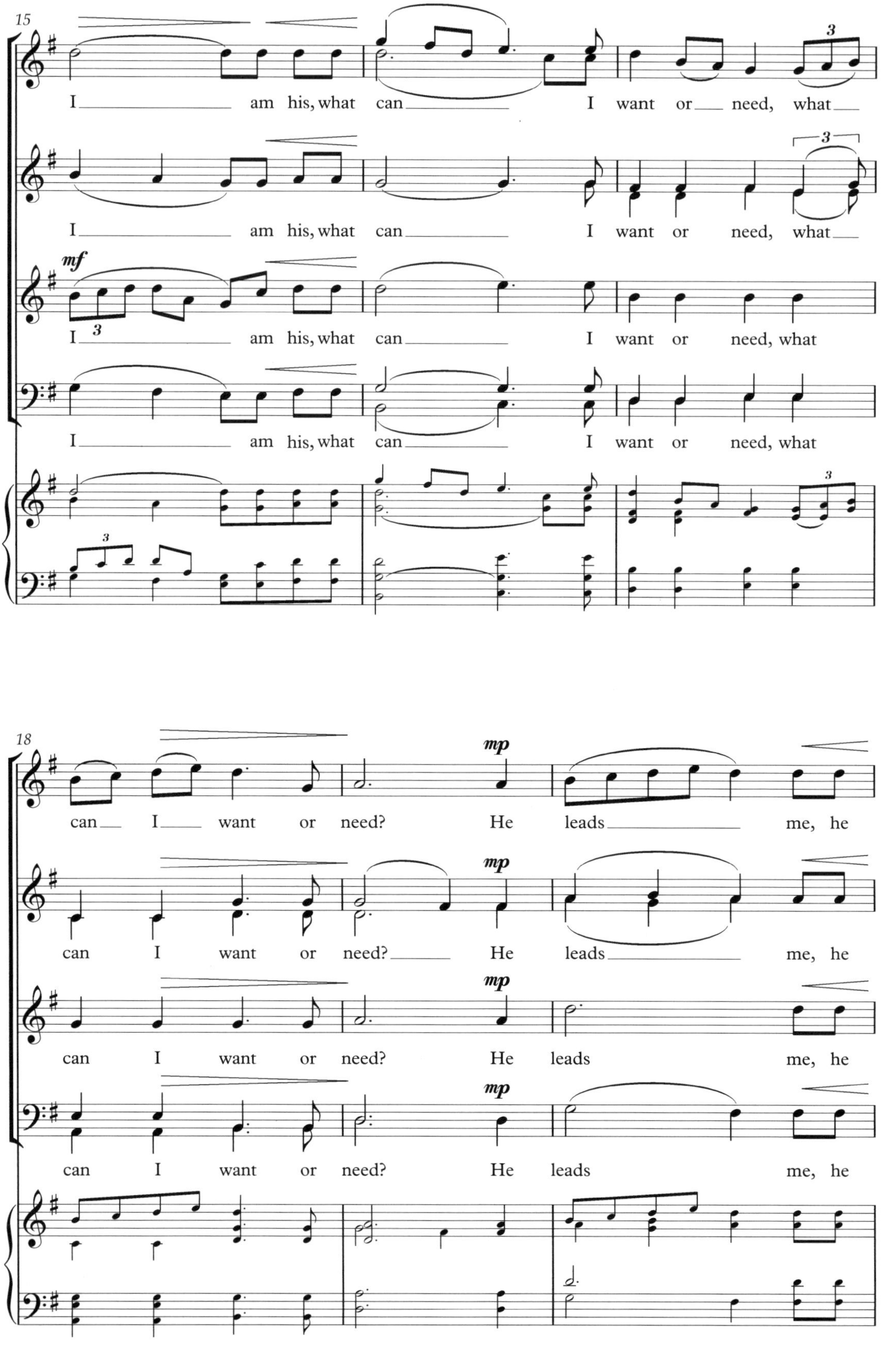

18
can I want or need? He leads me, he
can I want or need? He leads me, he
can I want or need? He leads me, he
can I want or need? He leads me, he
mp

21

leads me to the ten-der grass where I both feed and rest, then to the

leads me, leads me where I both feed and rest, then to the

mf

leads me, leads me where I both feed and rest, then to the

leads me, to the ten-der grass where I both feed and rest, then to the

24

streams that gent - ly passe: in both I

streams that gent - ly passe: in both I

streams that gen - tly passe: in both I

streams that gen - tly passe: in both I

27
mp
have the best. Or if I stray he doth con - vert and bring my mind in frame: and
have the best. Or if I stray he doth con - vert and bring my mind in frame: and
have the best. Or if I stray he doth con - vert and bring my mind in frame: and
have the best. Or if I stray he doth con - vert and bring my mind in frame: and
30
all this not for my des - ert but for his ho - ly name.
all this not for my des - ert but for his ho - ly name.
all this not for my des - ert but for his ho - ly name.
all this not for my des - ert but for his ho - ly name.

32
mf
Yea, in death's shad - y black a -
Yea, in death's black a - bode,
Yea, yea,
Yea,
Yea,
34
bode
well may I walk not fear;
yea, well may I walk,
yea,
yea,
yea,

37
yea, for thou art with me, for thy rod to
yea, for thou art with me,
yea, yea,
yea, yea, yea,
yea, yea, yea,
yea, yea, yea,
yea, yea,
41
mf
guide, thy staffe to bear. Nay, thou dost make me sit and dine, nay
yea. Nay, thou dost make me sit and dine, nay
yea. Nay, thou dost make me sit and dine, nay
yea. Nay, thou dost make me sit and dine, nay

45

sit and dine e- ven in my e-ne-mies' sight; my

sit and dine e - ven in my e-ne-mies' sight; my

thou dost make me sit and dine e - ven in my e-ne-mies' sight; my

sit and dine e - ven in my e-ne-mies' sight; my

48

head with oyl, my cup with wine, my cup with wine runnes

cup with wine, my cup with wine runnes

cup with wine, my head with oyl, my cup with wine runnes

cup with wine, my cup with wine runnes

50
rall.
o – – ver day and night, my cup runnes o – ver day and night.
o – – ver day and night, my cup runnes o – ver day and night.
o – – ver day and night, my cup runnes o – ver day and night.
o – – ver day and night, my cup runnes o – ver day and night.
Un poco meno mosso
52
mp espress.
Sure – ly thy sweet and won – drous love shall mea – sure all my days and
p espress.
Thy won – drous love shall mea – sure all my days and
p espress.
Thy won – drous love shall mea – sure all my days and
p espress.
Thy won – drous love shall mea – sure all my days and

molto rall. al fine
54
as it never shall remove, so neither, neither shall my praise.
as it ne - ver shall re - move, so nei - ther, nei - ther shall my praise.
as it ne - ver shall re - move, so nei - ther, nei - ther shall my praise.
as it ne - ver shall re - move, so nei - ther, nei - ther shall my praise.

7. The real presence

David Adam
from 'The Edge of Glory'

Margaret Rizza

This communion anthem may also be sung in an alternative unison version

(or UNISON)
13
mf
S
A
Lord, be with me in the break-ing of the bread. Lord, bless my heart, my
T
B
mf
pizz.
(or arco)
mf
16
cresc.
hands, my head. Lord, be with me, of-fer-ing the wine. Lord, bless bo-dy and
cresc.
(ossia)
cresc.
20
un poco rit.
a tempo
CELLO SOLO
mp
dim.
soul, they are thine.
dim.
un poco rit.
a tempo
dim.
mp

TENORS and BASSES
25
mf
Lord, pre-sent in the wine and bread. Stay with me, Lord, when I am fed.
mf

SOPRANOS and ALTOS
29
mf
un poco rit.
Bless the way by which I go; guide me in this world be - low.
un poco rit.

a tempo
33
VIOLIN
mf
a tempo
mp

DESCANT
37
mf
Ah,
ah,
S
A
mf
Lord, thou art there in bread and wine; a - round my life may
T
B
mf
mf
arco

40
f
ah,
f
thou en - twine. Bless O Lord, the life I lead, from
f
(ossia)
f

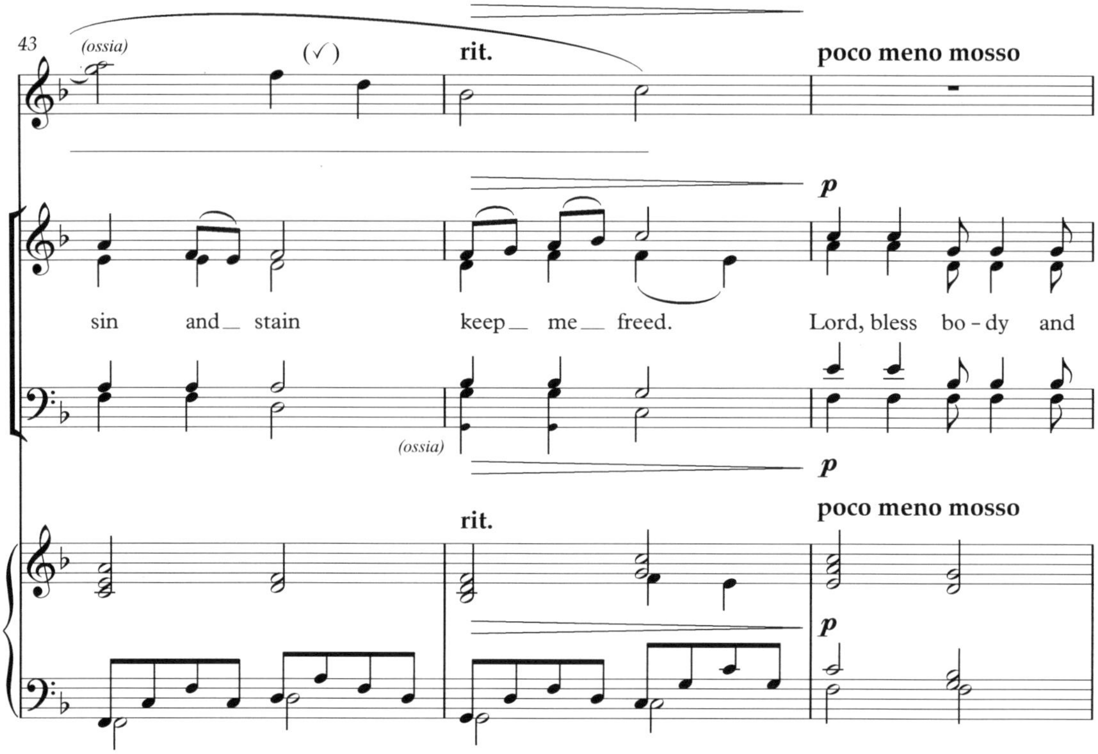

43
(ossia)
(✓)
rit.
poco meno mosso
p
sin and_ stain keep_ me_ freed. Lord, bless bo - dy and
(ossia)
p
rit.
poco meno mosso
p

46
molto rit.
soul, they are thine; Lord, bless bo - dy and soul, they are thine.
molto rit.

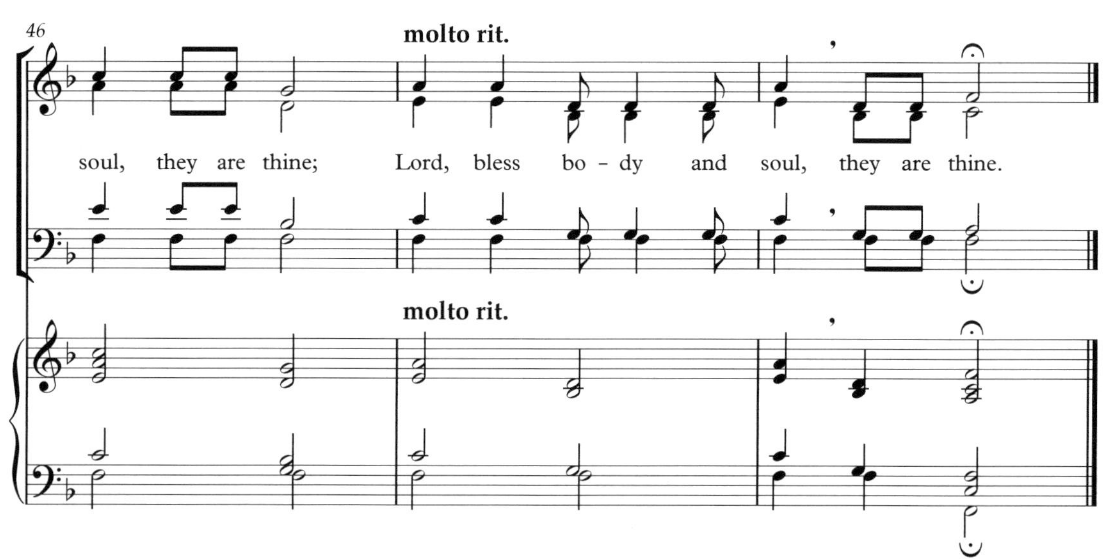

8. Gloria in excelsis

From Common Worship: Order One

Margaret Rizza

13
(✓)
peace to his peo - ple, peace to his peo-ple on earth.
17
S.
A.
T.
B.
f
Lord God, hea-ven-ly King, al-migh-ty God and
22
Fa - ther, we wor-ship you, we give __ you thanks, we praise you for your glo - ry.

27
Lord God, hea-ven-ly King, al-migh-ty God and Fa - ther, we
31
cresc.
wor - ship you, we give __ you thanks, we praise you for your glo - ry.
cresc.
cresc.
35
MELODY INSTRUMENT (C or B♭)
f
rall.
rall.
f

Meno mosso (♩ = c.60-66)
39
mp
S.
A.
(✓)
Lord Je - sus Christ, on - ly Son of the Fa - ther, Lord God,
T.
B.
mp
mp
42
Lamb of God, you take a - way the sin of the world: have
45
mer - cy, have mer - cy on us;

48
a tempo
mf
you are seat-ed at the right hand of the Fa - ther: re -
mf
a tempo
mf

51
ceive our prayer, re - ceive our prayer.
mf

54
un poco rit.
TRUMPET in B♭
f
f
For
f
un poco rit.

57
Tempo Primo (♩. = c.72-76)
(✓)
you a - lone are the Ho - ly One, you a - lone are the Lord,
f
2

61
f
(✓)
you a - lone are the Most High, you a - lone are the Most High,
f
2

65
Je - sus Christ, with the Ho - ly
2
2

70
SOPRANOS SEMI-CHORUS f
in the
Spi - rit, Je - sus Christ, with the Ho - ly Spi - rit, in the
75
a tempo
glo - ry, the glo - ry of God the Fa - ther, in the
glo - ry, the glo - ry of God the Fa - ther, in the
a tempo

79
glo - ry, the glo - ry of God the Fa - ther.
glo - ry, the glo - ry of God the Fa - ther.
cresc.
83
ff
A - men, a - men,
A - men, a - men,
ff

molto cresc. e rit. al fine
87
(ossia)
a,
a – – men.
molto cresc. e rit. al fine
a – – men,
a – – men.
molto cresc. e rit. al fine

Evening Prayer

9. Let my prayer rise before you

From Common Worship: Daily Prayer

Margaret Rizza

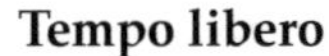

8
rall.
rall.
11
a tempo
mp
S
A
Let my prayer rise — be - fore you as —
T
B
mp
a tempo
14
3
in - cense; the lift - ing up of my hands — as the eve - - ning

più mosso
SOLO or UNISON
sac - ri - fice.
O Lord, I call to you; come to me quick - ly; hear my voice when I call to
più mosso
you.
SOLO or UNISON
rall.
Set a watch be - fore my mouth, O Lord, and guard the door of my
a tempo
Let my prayer rise be - fore you as in - cense; the
lips.
a tempo

28
lift - ing up of my hands as the eve - - ning sac - ri - fice.
3
3
3
3

SOLO or UNISON
32
mf
Let not my heart in - cline to a - ny e - vil thing; let me not be oc - cu - pied in
mf

un poco meno mosso
SOPRANO SOLO or UNISON
35
mp
wic - ked - ness with e - vil - do - ers. But my eyes are turned to you, Lord

38
rall.
S.A.
mf
God; in you I take ref - uge; do not leave me de-fence - less. Let my
T.B.
mf
rall.

a tempo
SOPRANO DESCANT or FLUTE / VIOLIN
42
f
prayer rise be - fore you as in - cense, my
f
prayer rise be - fore you as in - cense; the
f
a tempo
f

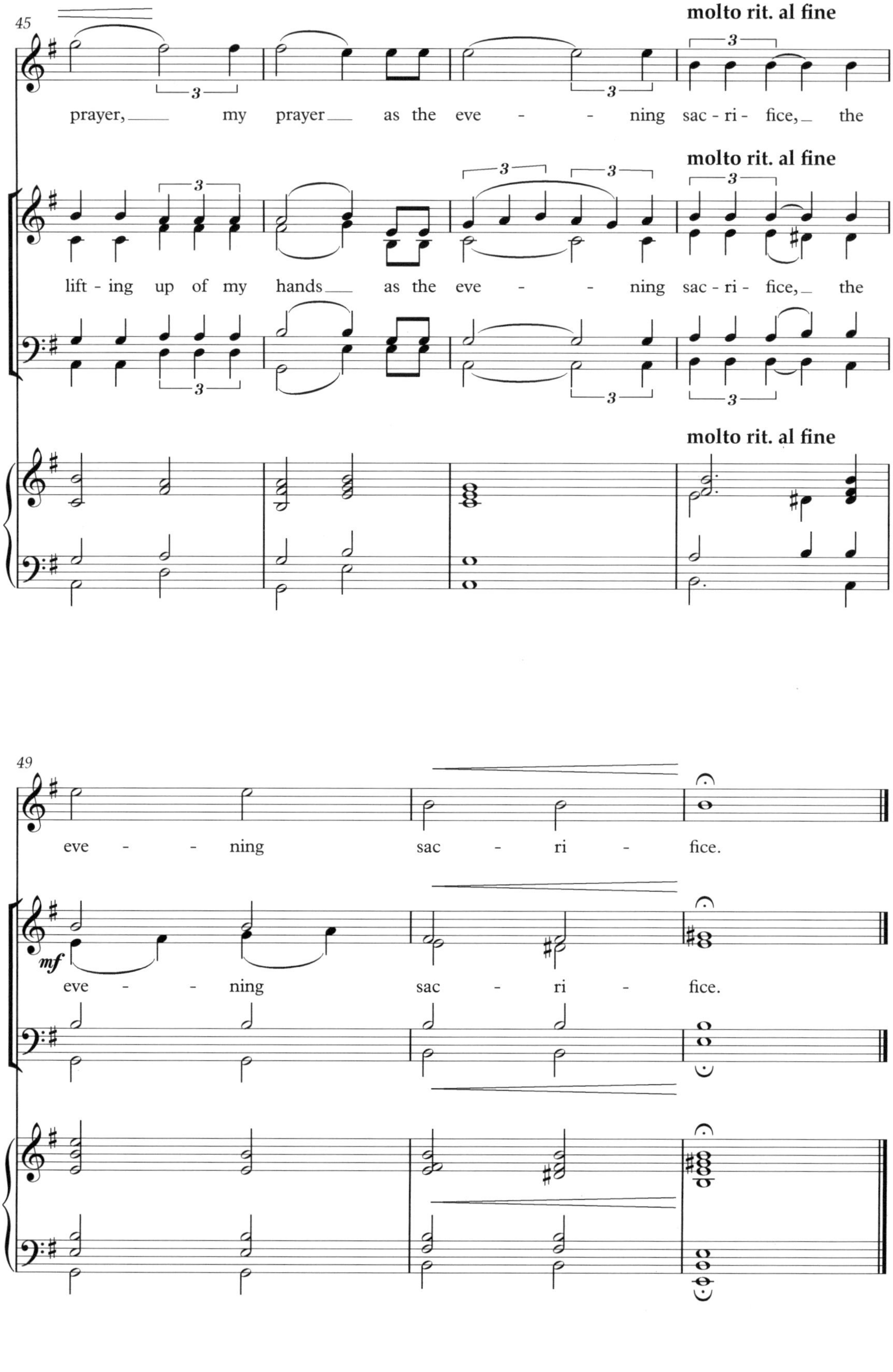

45

molto rit. al fine

prayer, my prayer as the eve - - ning sac-ri- fice, the

molto rit. al fine

lift-ing up of my hands as the eve - - ning sac-ri- fice, the

molto rit. al fine

10. Sweet dreams, form a shade

William Blake (1757—1827)

Margaret Rizza

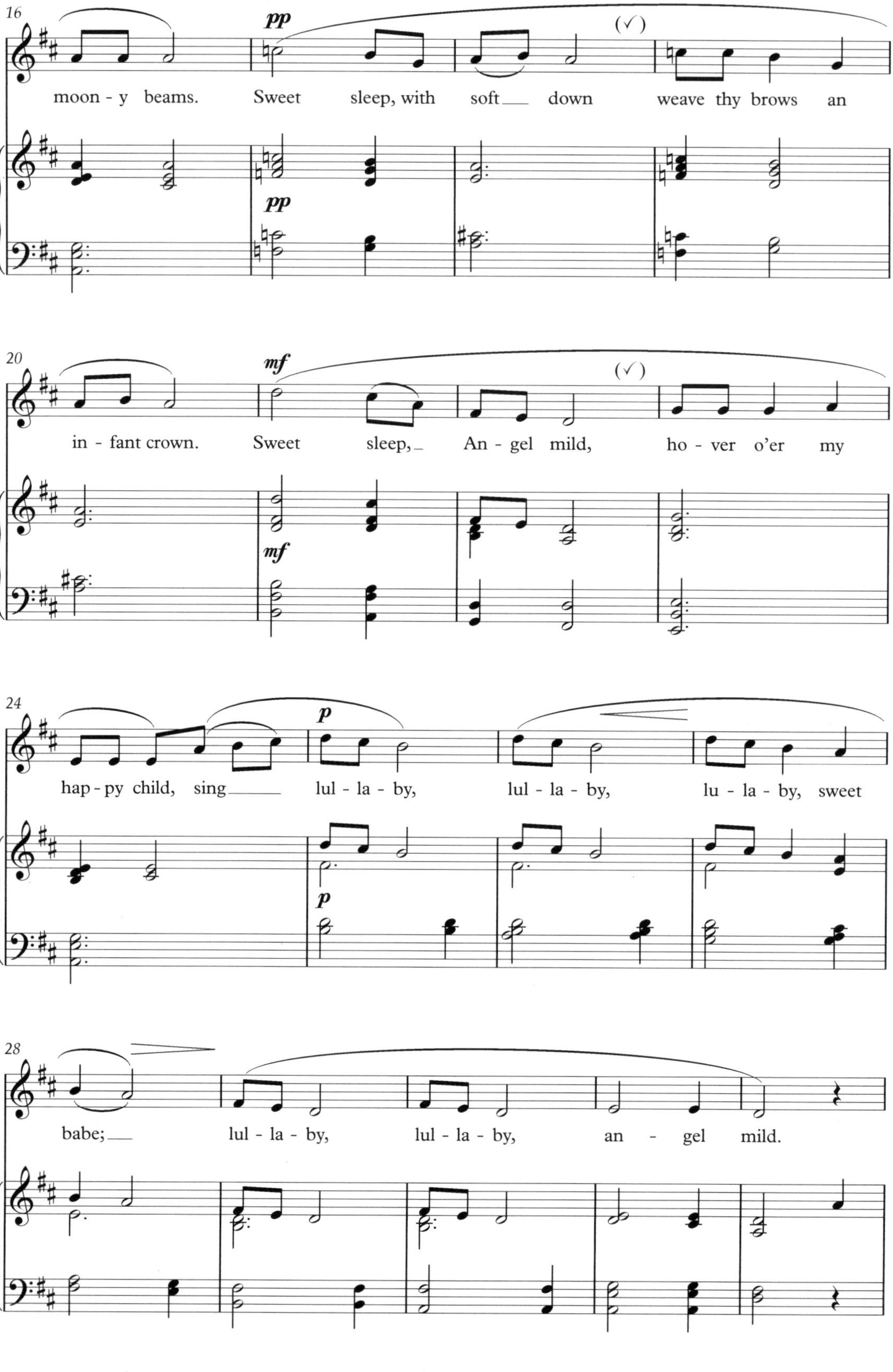
16
pp
(✓)
moon - y beams. Sweet sleep, with soft down weave thy brows an
pp
20
mf
(✓)
in - fant crown. Sweet sleep, An - gel mild, ho - ver o'er my
mf
24
p
hap - py child, sing lul - la - by, lul - la - by, lu - la - by, sweet
p
28
babe; lul - la - by, lul - la - by, an - gel mild.

un poco più mosso
33
FLUTE
mp
mf
38
un poco meno mosso
2
SOPRANO SOLO
(or SOPRANOS SEMI-CHORUS)
mp
(✓)
2. Sweet_ smiles, in the night
2
mp
43
(✓)
ho - ver o - ver my de - light; sweet smiles, Mo-ther's smiles,
47
pp
(✓)
all the live - long night be - guiles. Sweet moans,_ dove - like sighs,
pp

51
mf dolce espress.
chase not slum - ber from thy eyes. Sweet moans, sweet-er smiles,
mf
55
S.
A.
all the dove-like moans be-guiles, sing lul - la - by, lul - la - by,
all the dove-like moans be-guiles, sing lul - la - by, lul - la - by,
p
59
lu - la - by, sweet babe; lul - la - by, lul - la - by, an - gel mild.
lu - la - by, sweet babe; lul - la - by, lul - la - by, an - gel mild.

65
un poco più mosso
FLUTE

69
(FLUTE)
un poco meno mosso
2
S.
A.
mp
3. Sleep, sleep,
mp
3. Sleep, sleep,
2
mp

74
(✓)
hap-py child, all cre - a-tion slept and smiled; sleep, sleep, hap-py sleep, while
(✓)
hap-py child, all cre - a-tion slept and smiled; sleep, sleep, hap-py sleep, while

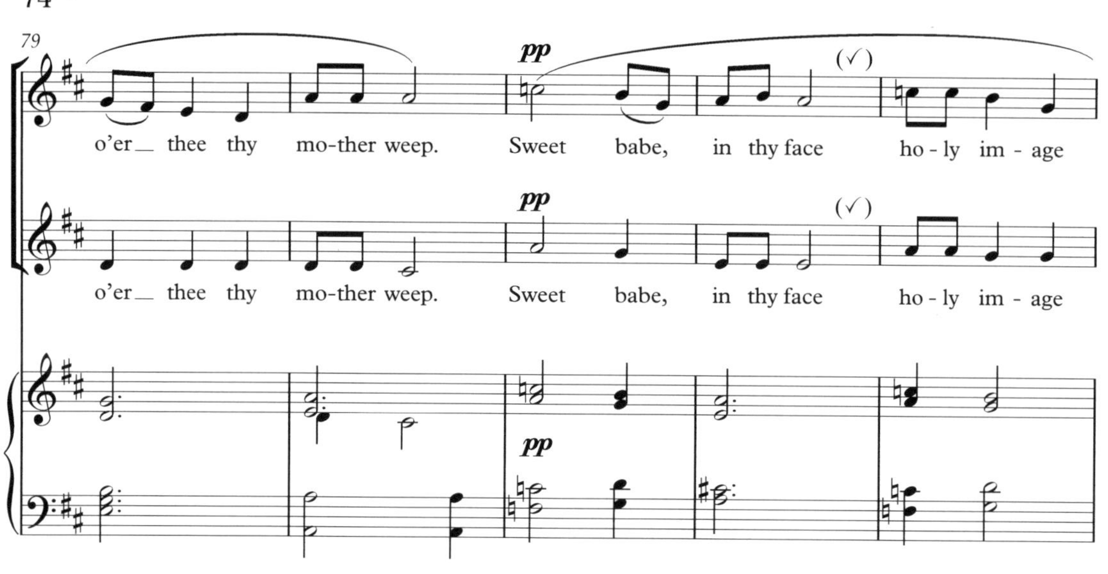
79
pp
(✓)
o'er_ thee thy mo-ther weep. Sweet babe, in thy face ho - ly im - age
pp
(✓)
o'er_ thee thy mo-ther weep. Sweet babe, in thy face ho - ly im - age
pp

84
mp
rall.
I can trace. Sweet babe,_ once like thee, thy mak - er lay and wept for me,
mp
I can trace. Sweet babe, once like thee, thy mak - er lay and wept for me,
mp

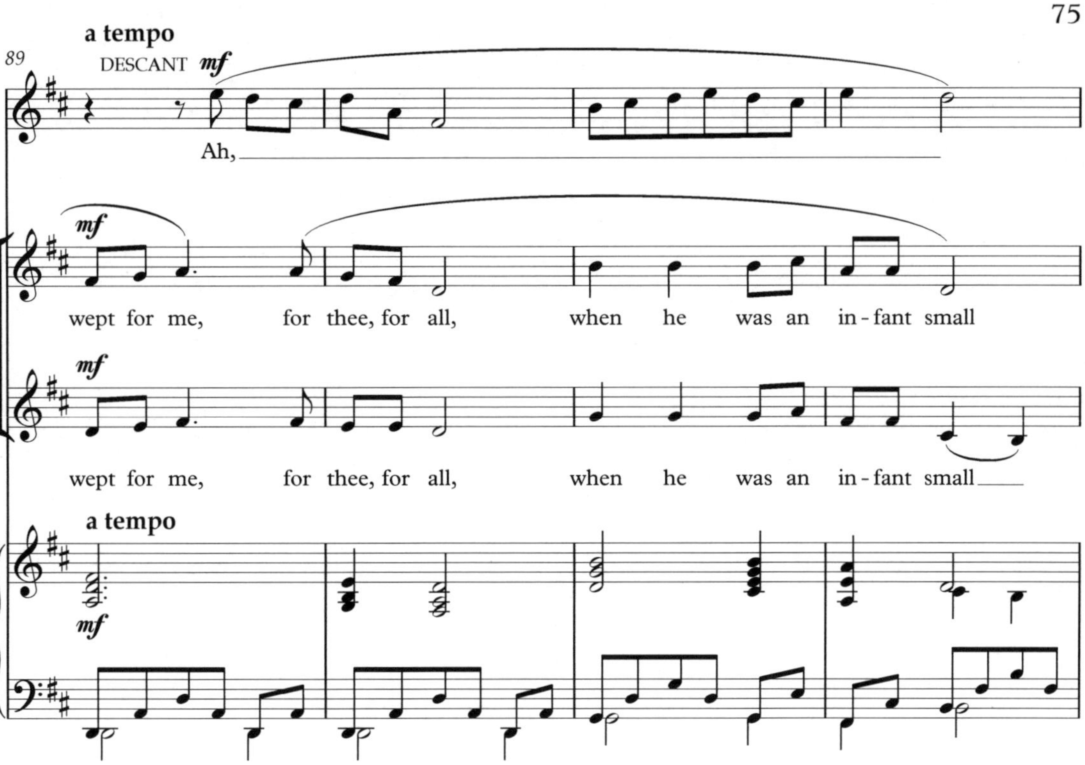
a tempo
89
DESCANT mf
Ah,
mf
wept for me, for thee, for all, when he was an in - fant small
mf
wept for me, for thee, for all, when he was an in - fant small
a tempo
mf

poco rit.
93
(✓)
ah,
(✓)
thou his im - age e - ver see, heav'n - ly face that smiles on thee,
(✓)
thou his im - age e - ver see, heav'n - ly face that smiles on thee,
poco rit.

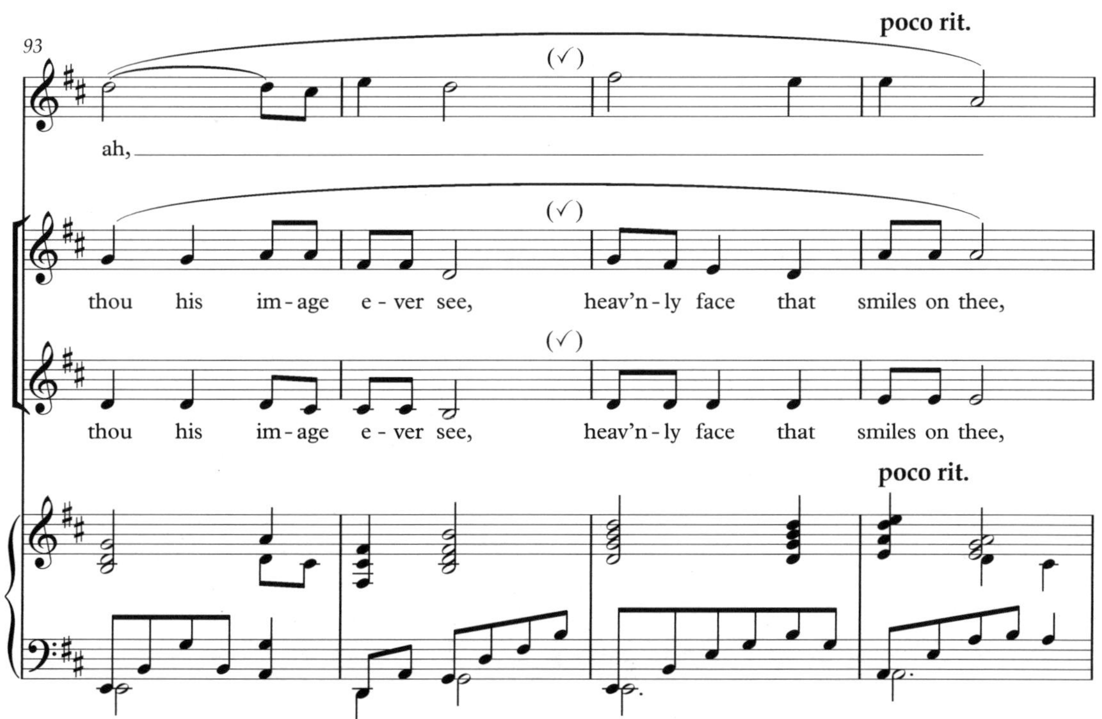

a tempo

97

mp dolce

ah, ah,

mp dolce

(✓)

smiles on thee, on me, on all; who be-came an in-fant small.

mp dolce

(✓)

smiles on thee, on me, on all; who be-came an in-fant small.

a tempo

mp

Largo

101

mf

(✓)

rall.

Meno mosso

ah,

S. SOLO
(or S. SEMI-CH.)

mf

(✓)

In - fant smiles are his own smiles; heav'n and earth to peace be-guiles. Sing

mf

(✓)

In - fant smiles are his own smiles; heav'n and earth to peace be-guiles.

Largo

rall.

Meno mosso

mf cresc.

105
pp
lul - la - by,
lul - la - by,
lu - la - by, sweet
babe;
pp

rall. al fine
dim. al fine
109
lul - la - by,
lul - la - by,
lul - la - by,
an - gel
mild.
dim. al fine

11. Song of Mary

Mary Holtby

Margaret Rizza

SOPRANOS and ALTOS
13
mp
ni - fi - cat, mag - ni - fi - cat a - ni - ma me - a, Do - mi - num. My name shall

17
live from age to age and ev - 'ry tongue his ser - vant bless. For mer - cy
mp

21
div. mf
is their he - ri - tage, whose hearts the Ho - ly One con - fess. Mag -

25
S.
A.
ni - fi-cat, mag - ni - fi - cat a-ni-ma me - a, Do - mi - num.
TENORS and BASSES
mf
T.
B.
The proud be -
mf
29
guiled by dreams of pow'r, di - vid - ed and de - grad - ed lie. He casts them
mf
33
S.
A.
Mag -
mp
Mag -
mf
T.
B.
down from throne and tow'r, and stoops to lift the hum-ble high. Mag -

ni - fi - cat Do - mi - num.
mp unis.
37
ni - fi - cat, mag - ni - fi - cat a - ni - ma me - a, Do - mi - num. He feeds the
3
ni - fi - cat Do - mi - num.
41
hun - gry at his board and sends the rich un - filled a - way.
And, mind ful
mp
pizz. (optional)
45
mf
Mag -
of his pro - mised word, has ans - wered Is - rael's pray'rs to - day.
mf

49

ni - fi-cat, mag - ni - fi - cat a-ni-ma me - a, Do - mi -
mf

52

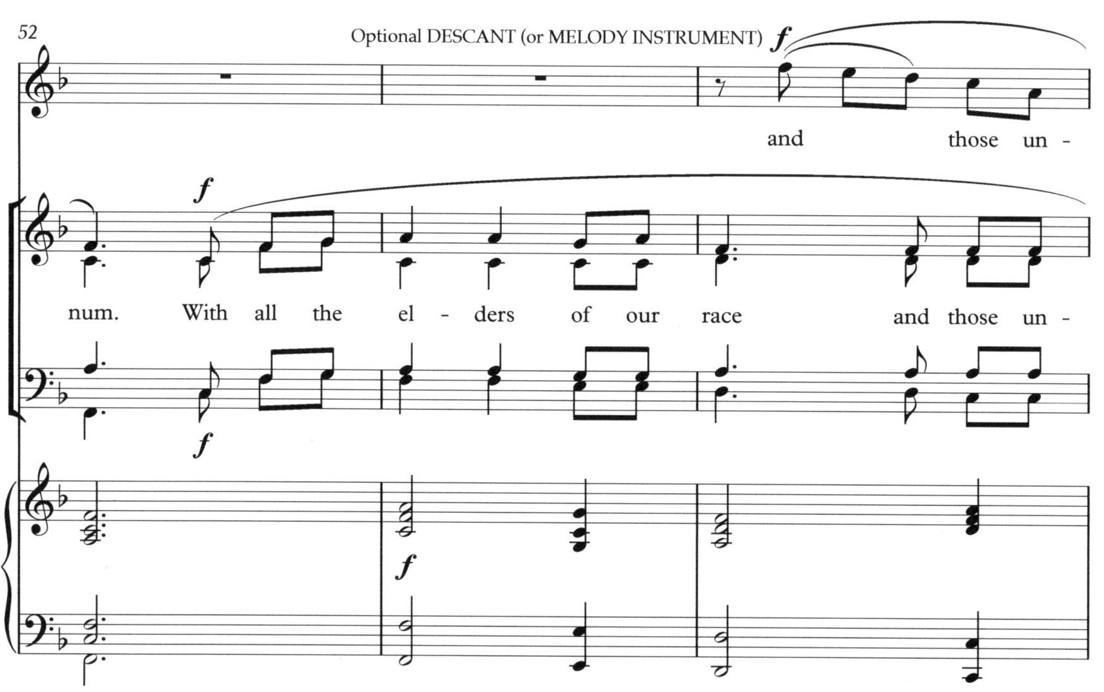
Optional DESCANT (or MELODY INSTRUMENT)
f
and those un -
f
num. With all the el - ders of our race and those un -
f
f

55
born who seek this birth, I sing the glo - ry of his
born who see this birth, I sing the glo - ry of his

58
race and bring e - ter - ni - ty to birth. Mag -
race and bring e - ter - ni - ty to earth. Mag -

61

ni - fi - cat, mag - ni - fi - cat a - ni - ma me - a, Do - mi -

ni - fi - cat, mag - ni - fi - cat a - ni - ma me - a, Do - mi -

f

rit. al fine

64

mp

num, a - ni - ma me - a, Do - mi - num.

mp

num, a - ni - ma me - a, Do - mi - num.

mp

rit. al fine

mp

12. Kindle in our hearts

From Common Worship: Daily Prayer

Margaret Rizza

T.B. SEMI-CHORUS
17
p
Kin-dle in our hearts, O God, the flame of love that ne - ver ceas - es,
pp
Hum
pp

21
that it may burn, burn in us, giv - ing light to o - thers.
Hum

25
2 FLUTES
p
SEMI-CHORUS
mp
S.
A.
Kin-dle in our hearts, O God,
SEMI-CHORUS mp
T.
B.
the flame of love that ne - ver ceas - es
p
S.
A.
Hum
T.
B.
p

29
that it may burn, burn in us, giv - ing light to o - thers.
Hum
33
FLUTES
mp
VIOLIN 2
mp
SEMI-CHORUS
mf
S.
A.
May we shine for e - ver in your tem - ple,
SEMI-CHORUS mf
T.
B.
set on fire with your e - ter - nal light.
mp
S.
A.
Ah
T.
B.
mp
Org.
mf
Ped.
CELLO (Optional)

37
e - ven your Son
Je - sus Christ, our Sa - viour and Re - deem - er.
Ah

41
FLUTES
mf
VIOLIN 2
mf
VIOLIN 1
f
f
May we shine for e - ver in your tem - ple, set on fire with your e - ter - nal love,
f
f
Set on fire, may we shine,
f

45
FLUTES
VIOLIN 2
VIOLIN 1
TRUMPET IN B♭
ff
e - ven your Son Je - sus Christ, our Sav - iour and Re - deem - er,
set on fire, may we shine,

49
f cresc. al fine
f cresc. al fine
f cresc. al fine
cresc. al fine
f cresc. al fine
may we shine for e - ver in your tem - ple, set on fire with
f cresc. al fine
f cresc. al fine
set on fire, may we
f cresc. al fine
f cresc. al fine

52
ff
your e - ter - nal love.
E - ven your Son
Je - sus Christ, our
shine,
set
on
fire,

55
rall.
molto rall.
div.
Sav - iour_ and Re - deem - er. A - men,
div.
may_ we_ shine,_ A - men,
rall.
molto rall.

58
a – – men, a – – men.
a – – men, a – – men.

Night Prayer

13. Before the ending of the day

From Night Prayer (Compline),
Common Worship: Daily Prayer

Margaret Rizza

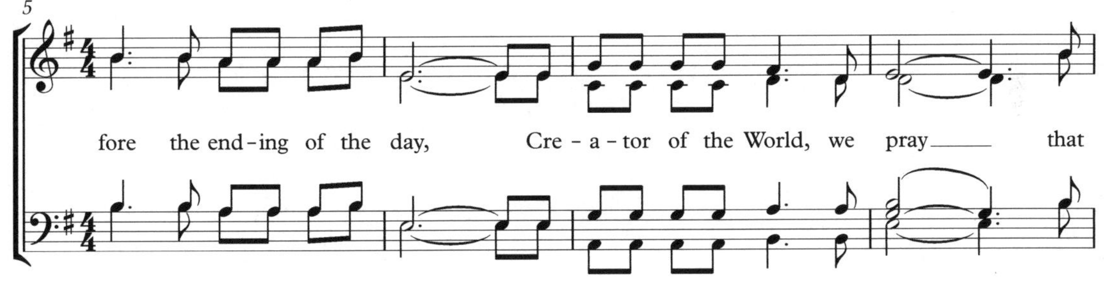

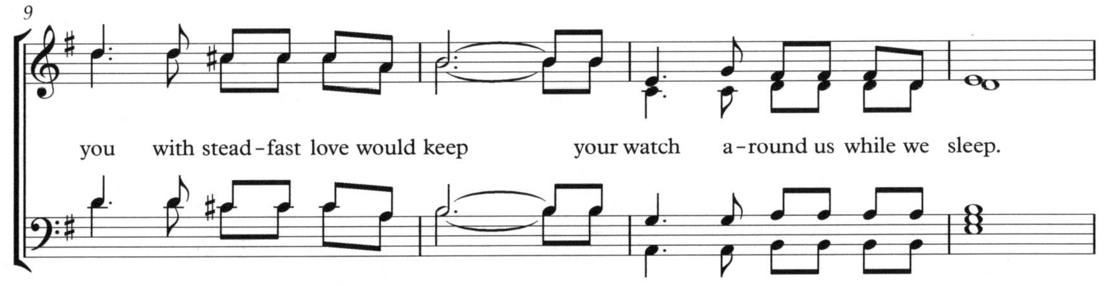

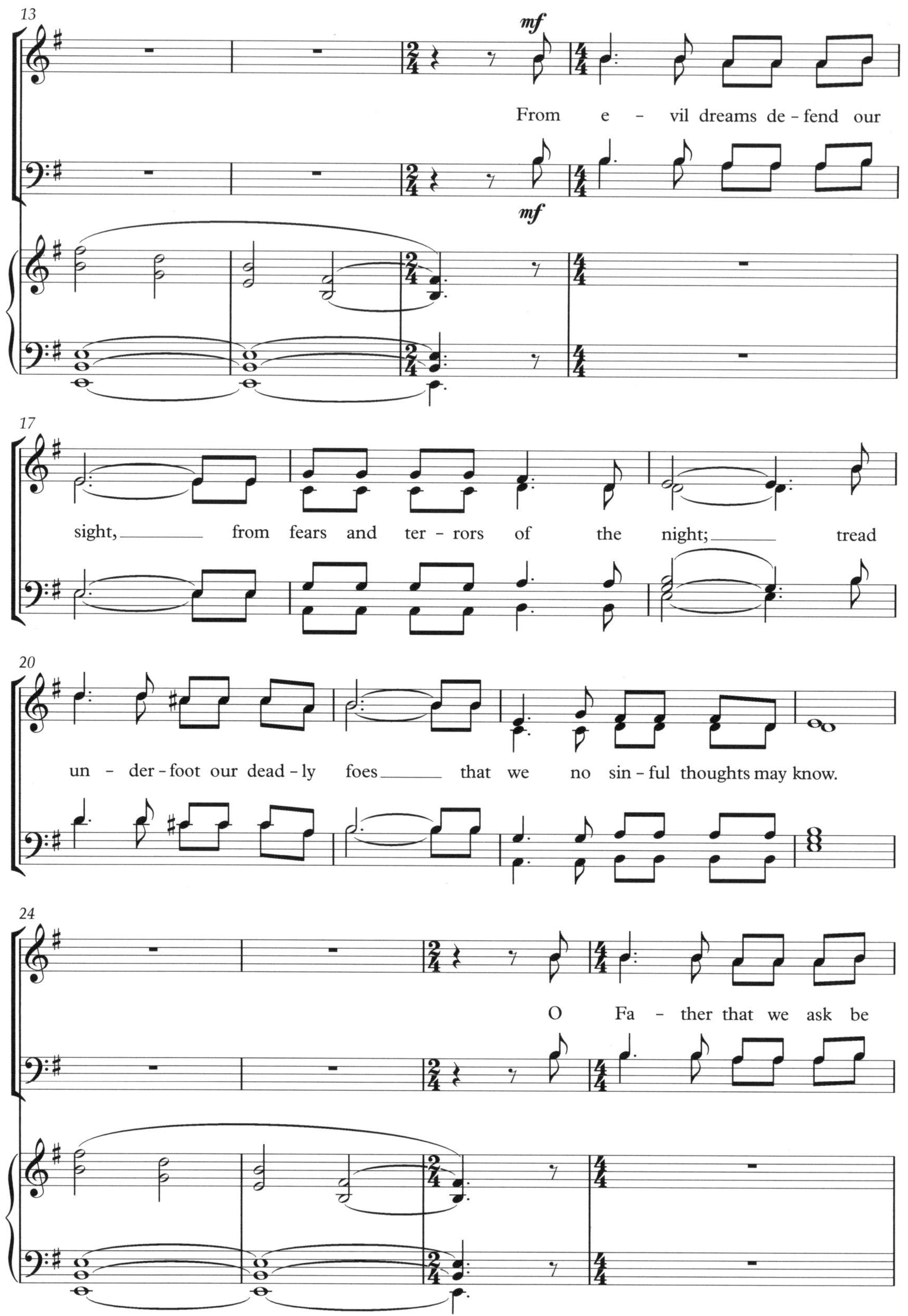
13
mf
From e - vil dreams de - fend our
mf
17
sight, from fears and ter - rors of the night; tread
20
un - der - foot our dead - ly foes that we no sin - ful thoughts may know.
24
O Fa - ther that we ask be

28
done through Je - sus Christ your on - ly Son; and
31
Ho - ly Spi - rit, by whose breath our souls are raised to life from death.
35

14. Keep me as the apple of your eye

From Night Prayer (Compline),
Common Worship: Daily Prayer

Margaret Rizza

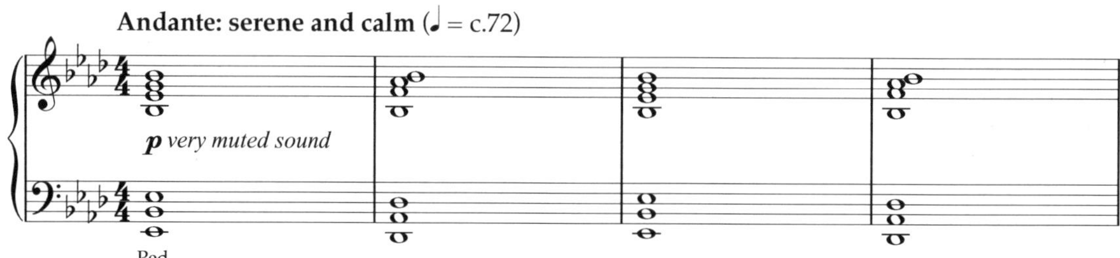

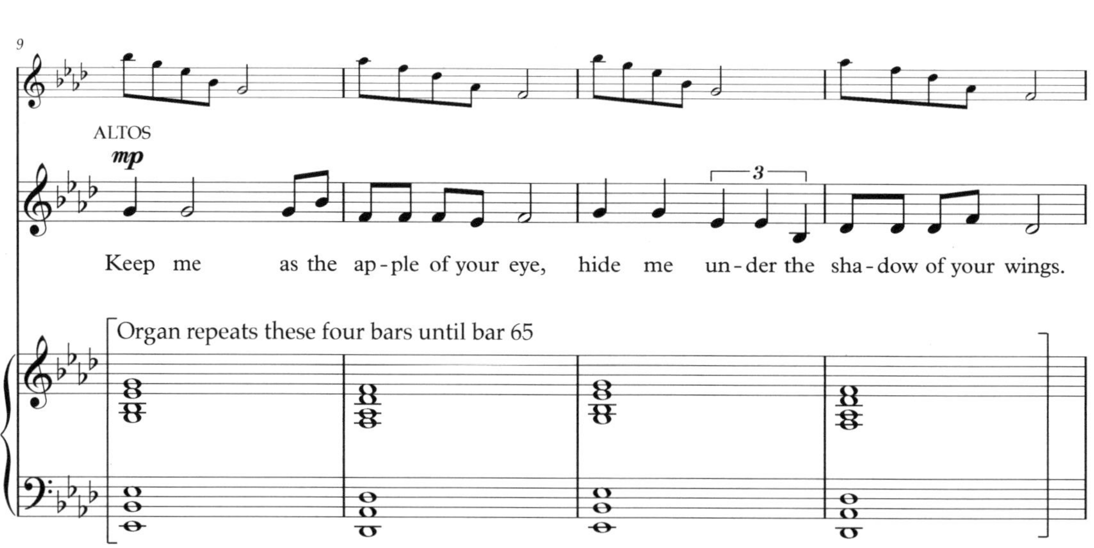

13
mf
mf
S.
Keep me as the ap-ple of your eye, hide me un-der the sha-dow of your wings.
A.
mf

17
mf
S.
A.
Keep me as the ap-ple of your eye, hide me un-der the sha-dow of your wings.
T.
B.
mf
CELLO
(SOLO VARIATION)
mf
mf

21
pp
Keep me, hide me; keep me, hide me.
pp

25
Keep me, hide me; keep me, hide me.
29
VIOLIN
mf
GUITAR
mp
(Sing words, or hum or 'ah')
mp
Keep me, hide me; keep me, hide me.
mp
mp
33
Keep me, hide me; keep me, hide me.

37
mf
mf
Keep me as the ap - ple of your eye, hide me un - der the sha - dow of your wings.
3
mf
mf
un poco più mosso
41
FLUTE 1
mp leggiero
pp
Keep me, hide me; keep me, hide me.
pp
mp
45
(ossia)
Keep me, hide me; keep me, hide me.

49
FLUTE 1
mf
FLUTE 2
mf
Keep me, hide me; keep me, hide me.
53
molto rit.
molto rit.
Keep me, hide me; keep me, hide me.
Tempo I
57
GUITAR
mf
ALL VOICES
mf
3
Keep me as the ap-ple of your eye, hide me un-der the sha-dow of your wings.

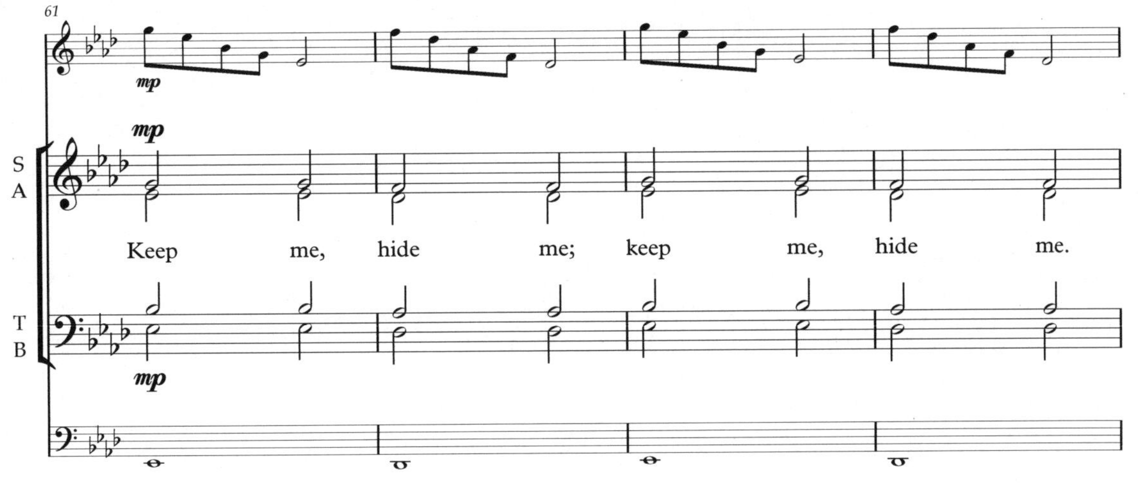
61
mp
S
A
Keep me, hide me; keep me, hide me.
T
B
mp

65
dim. e rit. al fine
dim. e rit. al fine
(or Hum)
Keep me. hide me. Hum
dim. e rit. al fine

15. Song of Simeon

Mary Holtby

Margaret Rizza

Flessibile ♩ = 66

ALL VOICES: UNISON

mf

Lu - men ad re - ve - la - ti - o - nem gen - ti - um; il -

3

lu - mi-na te - ne - bras nos - tras Do - - mi - ne.

un poco più mosso

TENORS and BASSES (or SOLO)

6

mf

Lord, set your ser-vant free, ful - fil your an - cient vow; and peace-ful let the

un poco più mosso

mf

OPTIONAL CELLO

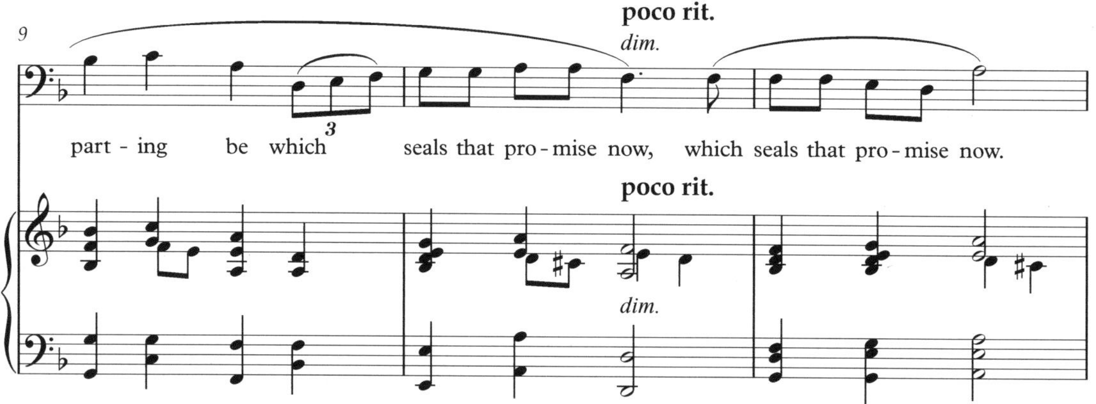

a tempo
12
mf
S.
A.
Lord, set your ser-vant free, ful-fil your an - cient vow and
T.
B.
mf
a tempo
pizz. (optional)
rit.
15
(✓)
peace - ful let the part-ing be which seals that pro - mise now.
rit.
a tempo
ALL VOICES: UNISON
18
mf
Lu - men ad re - ve-la-ti - o-nem gen-ti-um; il -
SOPRANOS
and ALTOS
p
20
lu - mi-na te-ne - bras nos - tras Do - - mi - ne. From

23
here the child of light, the world's sal - va - tion lies and on the na - tions

26
un poco rit.
lost in night I see his dawn a - rise, I see his dawn a - rise.
un poco rit.

a tempo
Ah
29
pp
S.
A.
From here the child of light, the world's sal - va - tion lies and
mf
T.
B.
pp
Ah
a tempo
OPTIONAL ACCOMPANIMENT
OPTIONAL CELLO

* Or doubled by a melody instrument, or with just a melody instrument on the descant line.

43
hu - man - kind, the glo - ry of our race, the glo - ry of our race;
hu - man - kind, the glo - ry of our race, the glo - ry of our race;

46
ff
ra - diance un - con - fined to change of time or place, he
ff
ra diance un - con - fined to change of time or place, he
ff
ff

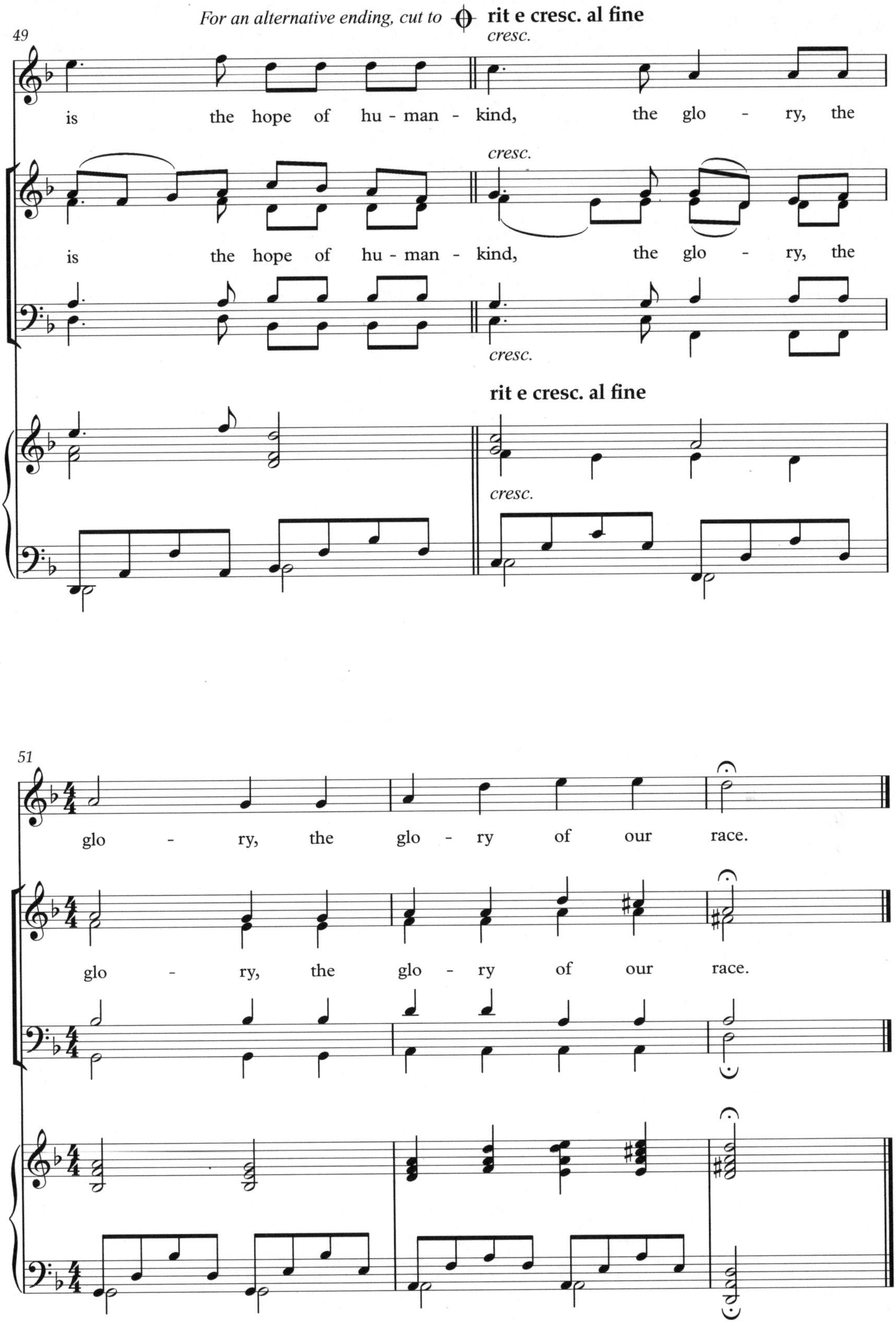

For an alternative ending, cut to ⊕ **rit e cresc. al fine**

49

cresc.

is the hope of hu - man - kind, the glo - ry, the

cresc.

is the hope of hu - man - kind, the glo - ry, the

cresc.

rit e cresc. al fine

cresc.

Alternative ending

a tempo

ALL VOICES: UNISON

54 *mf*

Lu - men ad re - ve - la - ti - o - nem gen - ti - um; il -

rit. al fine

56

lu - mi-na te - ne - bras nos - tras Do - - mi - ne.

16. Night prayers

David Adam,
from 'The Edge of Glory'

Margaret Rizza

11
FLUTE 1
mf
(ossia)
GUITAR (8va ad lib.)
mf
that re - freshed, I may wake to work a - gain for thee.
mf

14
(ossia)
FLUTE 2 or VIOLIN
mf
Org. LH or CELLO pizz.

18
un poco più mosso
21
mp
S.
A.
God in the night,
God at my right,
God all the day,
T.
B.
mp
24
mf
God with me stay.
God,
God,
God in my heart,
ne - ver de - part,
2
f
God,
God,
27
f
rall.
God with thy might
keep us in light
through this dark night.

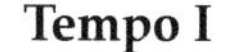

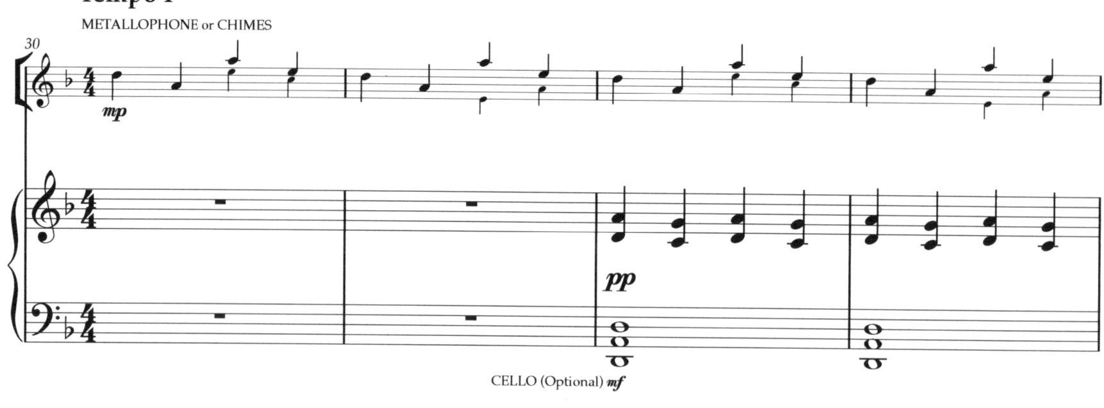
Tempo I
METALLOPHONE or CHIMES
30
mp
pp
CELLO (Optional) mf

34
MEN (or ALL unison)
mf
As I take my rest, Spi-rit, keep me with the blest;
WOMEN (or ALL unison)
ho-ly bles-sed three, keep me
p

37
ALL mf
close to thee. As I en-ter in-to sleep, keep me, Fa-ther, keep;
mf

40
rit. al fine
mp
as I seek a safe re-pose, Christ my eye-lids close. Christ my eye-lids close,
mp

sempre molto rit.
43
p
pppp
pppp
Christ my eye-lids close, my eye - lids close, my eye - lids close.
pppp